CONTENTS

GRADE 6

P9-BZW-152

ISBN: 978-1-927042-15-1

1 Operations with Whole Numbers

WORDS TO LEARN

Place value – the position of a number showing its value

$$362\ 849 = 300\ 000 + 60\ 000 + 2000 + 800 + 40 + 9$$

Order of operation – the operations must be done in the following order:

1st: Do multiplication or division from left to right.

2nd: Do addition or subtraction from left to right.

e.g. $17 + 25 \times 2$ $17 + 25 \times 2$

$= 42 \times 2$ $= 17 + 50$

$= 84$ ✗ $= 67$ ✔

Hundred Thousands	Ten Thousands	Thousands	Hundreds	Tens	Ones
3	6	2	8	4	9

Remember to do multiplication or division first.

Look at each number. Fill in the blanks and write each number in expanded form.

130 201

① 3 is in the ___ten thousands___ column; it means ___30,000___ .

Expanded form: ___100,000 + 30,000 + 200 + 1___

600 113

② 6 is in the ___hundred thousands___ column; it means ___600,000___ .

Expanded form: ___600,000 + 100 + 10 + 3___

782 003

③ 2 is in the ___thousands___ column; it means ___2000___ .

Expanded form: ___700,000, 80,000 + 3___

Put ">" or "<" in the circles.

④ 631 068 ⬤< 633 860   ⑤ 605 328 ⬤< 650 328

⑥ 134 165 ⬤< 134 516   ⑦ 864 173 ⬤> 846 173

⑧ 276 003 ⬤> 267 300   ⑨ 509 619 ⬤< 510 691

Canadian Curriculum MathSmart (Grade 6)   ISBN: 978-1-927042-15-1

Write the numbers.

⑩   10 thousand greater than 956 430   966,430

⑪   100 thousand less than 654 739   554,739 ~comma

⑫   100 thousand greater than 504 762   604,762

⑬   10 thousand less than 790 653   780,653

Find the answers.

⑭
```
    1 2 1
    4 1 0
    2 1 3
 +  1 0 5
  ─────────
    8 4 9
```

⑮
```
    2 3 2
    5 2 8
    3 7 9
 +  1 1 0
  ─────────
   1 2 4 9
```

⑯
```
   1 4 2 5
   1 2 3 7
     4 2 2
 +   6 7 9
  ─────────
   3 7 6 3
```

⑰
```
   3 6 2 8 4
 -     2 1 7 5
  ─────────────
   3 4 1 0 9
```

⑱
```
   4 0 1 5 9
 -   1 0 9 7
  ─────────────
   4 1 2 5 6
```

⑲   38 017 – 1784 = 37233

⑳   3647 + 825 + 163 + 249 = 4635

㉑   20 011 – 5200 = 48011

㉒   768 + 2593 + 1642 + 96 = _____

Estimate the answer by rounding each number to the nearest thousand. Then find the exact answer.

Round the number to the nearest thousand.

1103   Look at the digit in the hundreds column. If it is 5 or greater, round the number up. If it is less, round it down.
rounded to
1000

㉓   892 + 916 + 1094 + 1103 = _____

    (Estimate) _____

㉔   2798 + 552 + 1211 + 3079 = _____

    (Estimate) _____

㉕   37 603 – 8343 = _____

    (Estimate) _____

1

Mr. Morgan, the toy factory owner, wants to know the total number of cars in the boxes. Help him find the products.

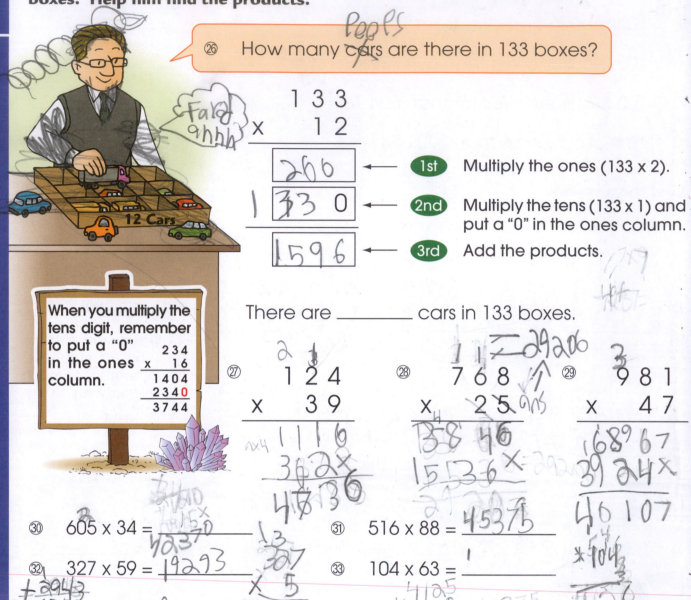

㉖ How many cars are there in 133 boxes?

$$\begin{array}{r} 1\,3\,3 \\ \times\ \ 1\,2 \end{array}$$

2 0 6 ← 1st Multiply the ones (133 x 2).

1 3 3 0 ← 2nd Multiply the tens (133 x 1) and put a "0" in the ones column.

1 5 9 6 ← 3rd Add the products.

When you multiply the tens digit, remember to put a "0" in the ones column.

$$\begin{array}{r} 2\,3\,4 \\ \times\ \ 1\,6 \\ \hline 1\,4\,0\,4 \\ 2\,3\,4\,0 \\ \hline 3\,7\,4\,4 \end{array}$$

There are _____ cars in 133 boxes.

㉗
$$\begin{array}{r} 1\,2\,4 \\ \times\ \ 3\,9 \end{array}$$

㉘
$$\begin{array}{r} 7\,6\,8 \\ \times\ \ 2\,5 \end{array}$$

㉙
$$\begin{array}{r} 9\,8\,1 \\ \times\ \ 4\,7 \end{array}$$

㉚ 605 x 34 = _____

㉛ 516 x 88 = _____

㉜ 327 x 59 = _____

㉝ 104 x 63 = _____

Estimate the answer by rounding each number to the nearest ten. Then find the exact answer.

㉞ 439 x 27 = _____

(Estimate) _____

㉟ 771 x 52 = _____

(Estimate) _____

㊱ 617 x 45 = _____

(Estimate) _____

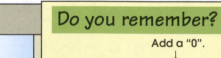

Do you remember?

Add a "0".

36 x 90 = 3240

$$\begin{array}{r} 3\,6 \\ \times\ \ \ 9 \\ \hline 3\,2\,4 \end{array}$$

If a number is multiplied by 10, 20, 30..., you can multiply the number by 1, 2, 3... and add a "0" to the end of the product.

ISBN: 978-1-927042-15-1

Read what Fiona the Cat says. Help her solve the problem. Then do the division.

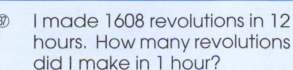

③⑦ I made 1608 revolutions in 12 hours. How many revolutions did I make in 1 hour?

$1608 \div 12 =$ _____

She made _____ revolutions.

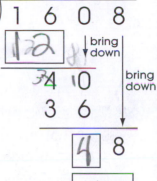

```
        1 3 4
   12) 1 6 0 8
       1 2        bring down
         4 0      bring down
         3 6
           4 8
           4 8
              0
```

5 steps to do division:

1st Estimate.
2nd Divide.
3rd Multiply.
4th Subtract.
5th Bring down.

③⑧
```
      1 3 1
  46) 4 6 9 2
      4 6
```

③⑨
```
      B 1 1
  39) 1 5 9 9
```

④⓪
```
  3 2 1  R 2 1
25) 8 4 6 7
```

④①
```
  1 4 2  R 1
18) 2 9 5 3
    1 8
```

④②
```
         R
23) 6 7 0 0
```

④③ $3591 \div 19 =$ _____

④④ $4026 \div 17 =$ _____

④⑤ $4815 \div 35 =$ _____

④⑥ $6912 \div 72 =$ _____

Use multiplication to check each division. Put a check mark ✔ in the box if it is correct. Write the correct answer if it is wrong.

④⑦ $4400 \div 36 =$ __125__ [X]

Check _____4500_____

④⑧ $5184 \div 24 =$ __216__ [✓]

Check _____5184_____

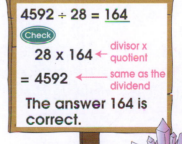

$4592 \div 28 = 164$

Check

28×164 ← divisor x quotient

$= 4592$ ← same as the dividend

The answer 164 is correct.

ISBN: 978-1-927042-15-1

There is a concert this evening. Help the children solve the problems.

㊾ How many hours did the children practise last week?

_____18_____ hours

We practised for 1080 min last week.

㊿ The concert hall is divided into 4 sections. The seats in these 4 sections are 452, 386, 415, and 339 respectively. How many seats are there in the concert hall in all?

_____1633_____ seats

452   386
415   339
867   725

(51) Each children's ticket costs $11. If 678 children attend the concert tonight, how much will be collected from selling children's tickets?

$ _____7458_____

(52) If all the tickets for the concert are sold out, how many adults are there in all?

_____ adults

(53) Each adult ticket costs $25. How much is collected from selling adult tickets?

$ _____

(54) How much more is collected from selling adult tickets than selling children's tickets?

$ _____

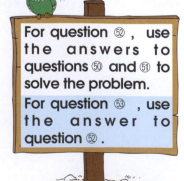

For question �52 , use the answers to questions ㊿ and �51 to solve the problem.
For question �53 , use the answer to question �52 .

Canadian Curriculum MathSmart (Grade 6)   ISBN: 978-1-927042-15-1

Find the answers.

⑤⑤ 14 + 21 × 2

= __14__ + __42__

= __56__

⑤⑥ 36 ÷ 3 – 11

= __12__ – __7__

= __5__

⑤⑦ 83 – 72 ÷ 9

= __83__ – __8__

= __75__

⑤⑧ 69 + 50 ÷ 5

= __69 + 10__

= __79__

⑤⑨ 91 – 4 × 17

= __91 + 68__
    + 68
    = 159

Do "×" or "÷" first.
Then do "+" or "–".

e.g.   3 + 8 ÷ 2
    = 3 + 4
    = 7   ← Do first.

$3 each

28¢ each

See what the children are going to buy. Help them solve the problems.

⑥⓪ Mike buys 3 bread rolls. If he pays with 90¢, what is the change?

The change is ____6____ ¢.

⑥① After buying 4 French loaves, Jason has $19 left. How much did Jason have at first?

Jason had $ ___31___ at first.

ACTIVITY

Look at the doughnuts in the box. Solve the problem.

The cost of the first 4 doughnuts is $3. For the remainder, each doughnut costs 50¢. How much does the box of doughnuts cost?

$ ___8___

2 Brackets

Brackets ( ) – signs to show which part of a problem is to be solved first

e.g. 5 x **(2 + 4)** = 5 x 6
= 30

Solve the problem inside the ( ) first.

Brackets must be used in pairs.

Read what Mrs. Martin and Janet say. Help them solve the problems.

① There were 25 students in my class. After transferring 3 girls to Mrs. Brown's class and 4 girls to Mrs. Winter's class, how many students are there in my class now?

$$25 - (3 + \underline{4}) = 25 - \underline{7}$$
$$= \underline{18}$$

There are __18__ students in Mrs. Martin's class now.

② I spend 15 min practising ballet in the morning and 20 min in the afternoon. How many minutes do I spend practising ballet from Monday to Friday?

$$(15 + \underline{20}) \times 5 = \underline{35} \times 5$$
$$= \underline{175}$$

Janet spends __175__ min practising ballet from Monday to Friday.

Find the answers.

③ (11 + 6) – 4
= __13 – 4 =__
= __13__

④ 4 x (16 – 9)
= __4 x 7 =__
= __28__

⑤ (42 + 6) ÷ 3
= __48 ÷ 3__
= __18__

⑥ 14 + (41 – 27)
= __14 + 14__
= __28__

⑦ (83 – 7) ÷ 2
= __76 ÷ 2__
= __38__

⑧ (15 + 5) x 8
= __20 x 8__
= __160__

Canadian Curriculum MathSmart (Grade 6)   ISBN: 978-1-927042-15-1

Place brackets in each number sentence to make it true.

⑨ 99 + (33 ÷ 11) = <u>102</u>

⑩ (108 − 3) x 9 = <u>945</u>

⑪ 14 x (7 + 6) = <u>182</u>

⑫ 256 ÷ (16 − 8) = <u>32</u>

⑬ 100 − (36 ÷ 4) = <u>91</u>

⑭ 39 + (2 x 17) = <u>73</u>

Fill in the blanks.

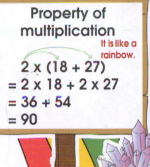

Property of multiplication

It is like a rainbow.

$2 \times (18 + 27)$
$= 2 \times 18 + 2 \times 27$
$= 36 + 54$
$= 90$

⑮ 7 x (3 + 5)

= 7 x <u>4</u> + 7 x <u>4</u>

= <u>28</u> + <u>28</u>

= <u>56</u>

⑯ 4 x (18 − 7)

= 4 x _____ − 4 x _____

= _____ − _____

= _____

⑰ (31 − 15) x 9

= _____ x 9 − _____ x 9

= _____ − _____

= _____

⑱ (50 + 2) x 5

= _____ x 5 + _____ x 5

= _____ + _____

= _____

ACTIVITY

See how the children can find the answers in a faster way. Follow their method to solve the problems.

4 x 82	Think: 82 = 80 + 2
= 4 x (80 + 2)	
= 4 x 80 + 4 x 2	
= 320 + 8	
= 328	

5 x 99	Think: 99 = 100 − 1
= 5 x (100 − 1)	
= 5 x 100 − 5 x 1	
= 500 − 5	
= 495	

① 6 x 91 = _____ (Think: 91 = 90 + 1)

② 9 x 59 = _____ (Think:)

③ 8 x 68 = _____ (Think:)

④ 7 x 42 = _____ (Think:)

⑤ 5 x 83 = _____ (Think:)

3 Integers

Integers – zero and all whole numbers
e.g. 20, -3, 0, 15, -1...

negative numbers   positive numbers

-4 -3 -2 -1 0 1 2 3 4

-3 and 3 are both 3 units from 0.
-3 and 3 are opposites.

The temperature is 20°C below zero. It is -20°C.

0, 5, -2, 3, -6... are integers.

4 units   4 units

-4 -3 -2 -1 0 1 2 3 4

-4 and 4 are opposites.

Colour the snowballs with integers.

①
| 12 | 1.4 | -3 | 0 | $\frac{2}{7}$ | $1\frac{1}{6}$ |

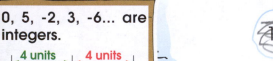

1.7   8   156   -8   10.01   20

Write the opposite of each integer.

②   +6 _____   ③   -15 _____   ④   -36 _____

⑤   +14 _____   ⑥   -9 _____   ⑦   +87 _____

Put ">" or "<" in the circles.

⑧   4 $>$ -2   ⑨   -8 $<$ -7   ⑩   -14 $<$ 2

⑪   2 $>$ 0   ⑫   1 $>$ -11   ⑬   -7 $<$ -6

Any integer is greater than those to its left.

-4 -3 -2 -1 0 1 2

e.g. -4 < -2, 0 < 1

Write the numbers in order from smallest to greatest.

⑭   -3   -6   5   0   2   6, -3, 0, 2, 5

⑮   5   -4   3   7   1   4-1, 3, 5, 7

⑯   1   0   -5   6   -3   5, -3, 0, 1, 6

Write the temperature of each city. Then answer the questions.

⑰

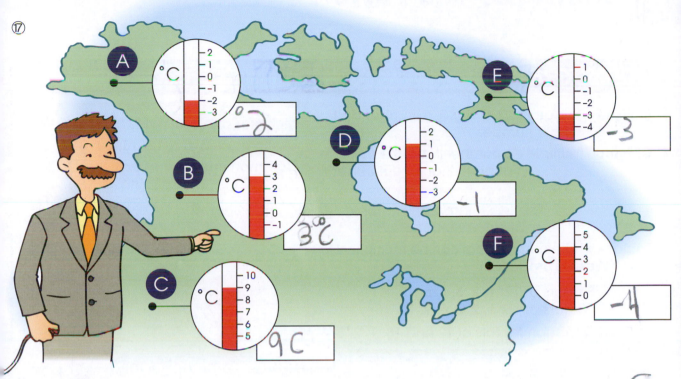

A ⟶ -2

E ⟶ -3

D ⟶ -1

B ⟶ 3°C

F ⟶ -4

C ⟶ 9 C

⑱ Which city has the highest temperature?   C

⑲ How many cities have temperatures below 0°C?   4

⑳ How many cities have temperatures above 0°C?   2

㉑ Which city has a temperature 8°C higher than that of D ?   C

㉒ Put the cities in order. Start with the lowest temperature.

-4° -3° -2° -1° 3° 4°

ACTIVITY

Fill in the missing integers with the help of the number line.

①   -5   -3   -1   1   3   5

②   4   2   0   -2   -4   -6

③   3   0   -3   -6   -9   -12

ISBN: 978-1-927042-15-1

4 Multiples and Factors

WORDS TO LEARN

Multiple – the product of a given number and a whole number

Common multiple – a number that is the multiple of more than one number

Multiples of 3: 3, 6, 9, **12**, 15, 18, 21, **24**...
Multiples of 4: 4, 8, **12**, 16, 20, **24**...
Common multiples of 3 and 4: 12, 24...

The least common multiple (L.C.M.) of 3 and 4 is 12.

Factor – whole number that can be multiplied to get a product

Factors of 12: **1**, **2**, **3**, 4, **6**, 12
Factors of 18: **1**, **2**, **3**, **6**, 9, 18
Common factors of 12 and 18: 1, 2, 3, 6

The greatest common factor (G.C.F.) of 12 and 18 is 6.

Which cans should Teddy aim for?
Write the numbers.

Ways to find multiples:

1. keep adding the numbers, or
2. multiply the numbers by 1, 2, 3...

① Teddy wants to throw the balls into every 2nd can.

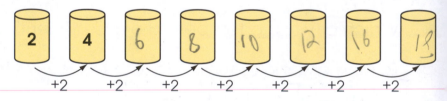

| 2 | 4 | 6 | 8 | 10 | 12 | 16 | 18 |

+2 +2 +2 +2 +2 +2 +2

② Teddy wants to throw the balls into every 3rd can.

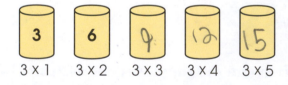

| 3 | 6 | 9 | 12 | 15 |

3 x 1   3 x 2   3 x 3   3 x 4   3 x 5

Write the first six multiples of each number.

③ 5 : 5 , 10 , 15 , 20 , 25 , 30

④ 7 : 7 , 14 , 21 , 28 , 35 , 42

⑤ 9 : 9 , 18 , 27 , 36 , 45 , 54

ISBN: 978-1-927042-15-1

Find the first eight multiples of each number. Then write the common multiple(s) and the L.C.M. of each pair of numbers.

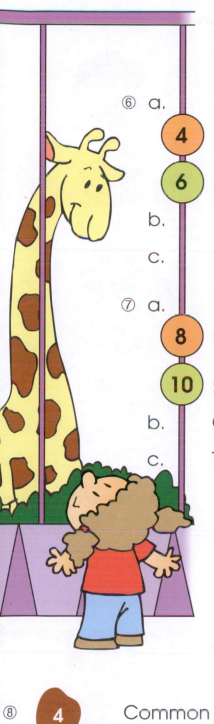

⑥ a.

4 : _4_ , _8_ , _12_ , _16_ , _20_ , _24_ , _28_ , _32_

6 : _6_ , _12_ , _18_ , _24_ , _30_ , _36_ , _42_ , _48_

b. Common multiples of 4 and 6: _12_ , _2_

c. The L.C.M. of 4 and 6: _12_

⑦ a.

8 : _8_ , _16_ , _24_ , _32_ , _40_ , _48_ , _56_ , _64_

10 : _10_ , _20_ , _30_ , _40_ , _50_ , _60_ , _70_ , _80_

b. Common multiple of 8 and 10: _40_

c. The L.C.M. of 8 and 10: _40_

List the multiples of each number. The first common multiple is their L.C.M.

Write the first four common multiples of the numbers. Then find the L.C.M.

⑧ **4** **5**

Common multiples: _9 18 27_

L.C.M.: _9_ ³ˣ 3 6 9 12 15 18 21 24 27 30 ...
9 18 27 36 45 54 63 72 81 ...

⑨ **3** **9**

Common multiples: _____

L.C.M.: _9_

⑩ **2** **6**

Common multiples: _____

L.C.M.: _____

ISBN: 978-1-927042-15-1

How many different groups of columns can Louis build with 14 blocks? Write the numbers.

All the groups of columns should have the same number of blocks.

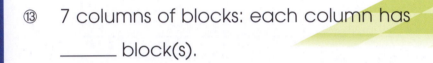

⑪ 1 column of blocks: each column has

_____ block(s).

14 = 1 x 14
14 = 2 x 7
14 = 7 x 2
14 = 14 x 1

⑫ 2 columns of blocks: each column has

_____ block(s).

⑬ 7 columns of blocks: each column has

_____ block(s).

⑭ 14 columns of blocks: each column has _____ block(s).

⑮ The factors of 14 are _____ , _____ , _____ , and _____ .

Find the factors of each number.

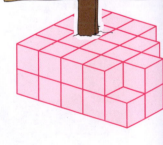

Stop when you get to a number you've already come across.
e.g. 6 = 1 x 6
      6 = 2 x 3
      6 = 3 x 2 ←
         Stop here!

⑯ 12 = 1 x __12__

12 = 2 x __6__

12 = 3 x __4__

⑰ 20 = 1 x __20__

20 = 2 x __10__

20 = 4 x __5__

The factors of 12 are:

12 3 4 6 12

The factors of 20 are:

1 2 4 5 10 20

⑱ The factors of 24 are: 1 2 3 4 6 8 12 24

⑲ The factors of 30 are: 1 2 3 5 6 10 30 15

⑳ The factors of 32 are: 1 2 4 8 16 32

㉑ The factors of 36 are: 1 2 4 9 12 18 36

㉒ The factors of 40 are: _____

ISBN: 978-1-927042-15-1

Find the factors of each number. Then write the common factors and G.C.F.

㉓ a.

20 : _1_ , _2_ , _4_ , _5_ , _10_ , _20_

28 : _1_ , _2_ , _4_ , _7_ , _14_ , _28_

b. Common factors of 20 and 28: _1_ , _2_ , _4_

c. G.C.F. of 20 and 28: _4_

㉔ a.

25 : _____ , _____ , _____

45 : _____ , _____ , _____ , _____ , _____ , _____

b. Common factors of 25 and 45: _____ , _____

c. G.C.F. of 25 and 45: _____

Find the common factors and G.C.F.

㉕ 30, 35 Common factors: _____

G.C.F.: _____

㉖ 48, 56 Common factors: _____

G.C.F.: _____

> List the factors of each number. Then find the common factors of the numbers. The greatest one is the G.C.F.

A C T I V I T Y

Help Freddie the Fish solve the problem.

> I want to make friends with 24 shrimps and 30 crabs. How many days would it take me to do that if I meet the same number of shrimps and the same number of crabs each day?

It would take _____ days. Freddie the Fish has to meet _____ shrimps and _____ crabs each day.

ISBN: 978-1-927042-15-1

5 Composite and Prime Numbers

Composite number – any number greater than 1 that has more than 2 factors
Prime number – any number with only 1 and itself as factors

8 has 4 factors. They are 1, 2, 4, and 8. 8 is a composite number.

8 is a composite number.

8 is a prime number. ✗

Help the children find the number of stickers in each group. Write "composite" or "prime".

$6 = 2 \times 3$; 6 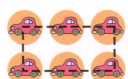 can form a rectangle.

6 is a ___composite___ number.

①

___ $= 1 \times 7$; 7 is a _____ number.

②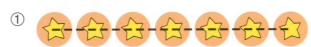

___ $= 1 \times 5$; 5 is a _____ number.

③  ___ $= 2 \times 2$;

4 is a _____ number.

If the number can form a rectangle, it is a composite number.

e.g. 10

10 is a composite number.

Write "prime" or "composite" for each number.

④ 21 _____ ⑤ 19 _____ ⑥ 30 _____

⑦ 43 _____ ⑧ 65 _____ ⑨ 74 _____

Canadian Curriculum MathSmart (Grade 6)   ISBN: 978-1-927042-15-1

Follow the children's way to write each number as a product of prime factors.

Steps to write numbers as a product of prime factors:

1st Write the composite number as the product of two factors.

2nd Continue to factorize each composite number until all factors are prime numbers.

3rd Write the number as a product of prime factors.

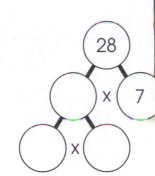

$30 = 2 \times 3 \times 5$

The number "1" is not used in the factor tree.

⑩

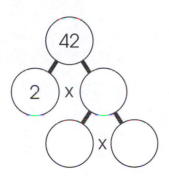

42 = _____

⑪

28 = _____

⑫

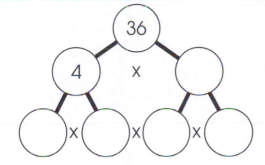

36 = _____

⑬

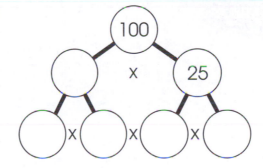

100 = _____

⑭ 66 = _____

⑮ 52 = _____

⑯ 74 = _____

⑰ 96 = _____

⑱ 81 = _____

⑲ 88 = _____

⑳ 32 = _____

㉑ 40 = _____

㉒ 24 = _____

㉓ 58 = _____

Follow the steps to find the greatest common factor (G.C.F.) of each pair of numbers.

Find the G.C.F. of 18 and 30.

18 = 2 x 3 x 3
30 = 2 x 3 x 5

Common prime factors: 2, 3
The G.C.F. of 18 and 30: 2 x 3 = 6

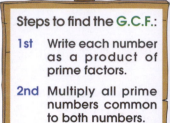

Steps to find the G.C.F.:

1st   Write each number as a product of prime factors.

2nd   Multiply all prime numbers common to both numbers.

㉔ 30 = ___ X ___ X ___

45 = ___ X ___ X ___

Common prime factors: ___ , ___

G.C.F.: ___ x ___ = _____

㉕ 48 = ___ X ___ X ___ X ___ X ___

72 = ___ X ___ X ___ X ___ X ___

Common prime factors: ___ , ___ , ___ , ___

G.C.F.: ___ x ___ x ___ x ___ = _____

Write each number as a product of prime factors. Then find the G.C.F.

㉖ 12 = _____

20 = _____

G.C.F.: _____

㉗ 15 = _____

60 = _____

G.C.F.: _____

㉘ 8 = _____

40 = _____

G.C.F.: _____

㉙ 56 = _____

64 = _____

G.C.F.: _____

ISBN: 978-1-927042-15-1

Follow the steps to find the least common multiple (L.C.M.) of each pair of numbers.

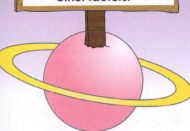

Steps to find the L.C.M.:

1st Write each number as a product of prime factors.

2nd Sort out the common prime factors and multiply them to all other factors.

Find the **L.C.M.** of 16 and 20.

$16 = \boxed{2} \times \boxed{2} \times \boxed{2} \times \boxed{2} \boxed{}$

$20 = \boxed{2} \times \boxed{2} \times \boxed{5}$

L.C.M.: $2 \times 2 \times 2 \times 2 \times 5 = 80$

㉚   10 = ___ x ___

66 = ___ x ___ x ___

L.C.M.: ___ x ___ x ___ x ___

= _____

 ㉛   **35** = ___ x 7

50 = ___ x ___ x ___

L.C.M.: ___ x ___ x ___ x ___

= _____

㉜   **15** = ___ x ___

21 = ___ x ___

L.C.M.: ___ x ___ x ___

= _____

Find the L.C.M. of each pair of numbers.

㉝   10   15
L.C.M. : _____

㉞   8   20
L.C.M. : _____

㉟   9   24
L.C.M. : _____

㊱   18   27
L.C.M. : _____

㊲   22   33
L.C.M. : _____

㊳   27   72
L.C.M. : _____

 A C T I V I T Y

Read what Roger says. Then try out Goldbach's theory on the following numbers.

① 24 = _____ + _____

② 76 = _____ + _____

③ 90 = _____ + _____

 A mathematician called Goldbach believed that all even numbers can be made by adding 2 prime numbers. e.g. 10 = 7 + 3; 8 = 5 + 3

6 Time, Speed, and Distance

WORDS TO LEARN

a.m. – any time between midnight and midday (noon)

p.m. – any time between midday and midnight

24-hour clock time – telling times by using numerals only

e.g. 06:30 means 6:30 a.m.; 17:45 means 5:45 p.m.

Speed – how fast an object moves

$$\text{Speed} = \frac{\text{Distance}}{\text{Time}}$$

I travel 2400 km in 2 h. My speed is 1200 km/h.

Write the times in 24-hour clock times.

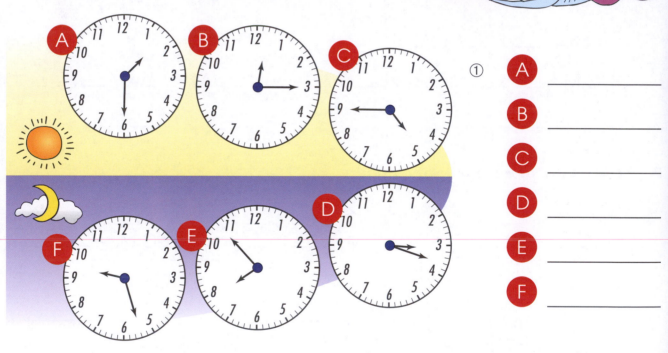

① A _____

B _____

C _____

D _____

E _____

F _____

Write the times using "a.m." or "p.m.". Then draw the clock hands to show the times.

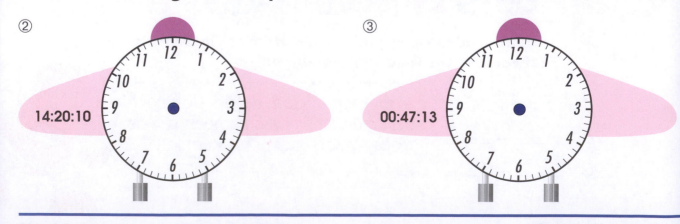

② 14:20:10

③ 00:47:13

Canadian Curriculum MathSmart (Grade 6)   ISBN: 978-1-927042-15-1

Pearson International Airport

Flight	From	Scheduled Time	Arrival Time
CC34	Chicago	09:35	10:00
CP826	Munich	11:50	
CA68	New York		17:15
CA55	Vancouver	23:35	00:15

Look at the timetable. Solve the problems.

④ Did Flight CC34 arrive at the airport at night?

_____

⑤ By how many minutes was Flight CA55 delayed?

_____

⑥ What was the arrival time of Flight CP826 if there was a delay of 25 minutes?

_____

⑦ The arrival time of Flight CA68 was 36 minutes earlier than the scheduled time. What was the scheduled time?

_____

Peter and his father are at the airport. Help them solve the problems.

⑧ If Peter and his father arrived at the airport at 11:45, how long have they waited for Uncle Tim?

12:53

_____

⑨ Which flight did Uncle Tim probably take?

_____

⑩ How long did it take Uncle Tim to go through customs?

_____

For question ⑩, you have to use the answer to question ⑥. Use subtraction to solve the problem.

ISBN: 978-1-927042-15-1

6

Choose the most appropriate units to record the distances between the things or the lengths of the things. Write "km", "m", "dm", "cm", or "mm".

⑪

Do the conversions.

⑫ 63 cm = _____ mm   ⑬ 4 km = _____ m

⑭ 9.2 m = _____ dm   ⑮ 5.7 dm = _____ cm

⑯ 97 dm = _____ m   ⑰ 2300 m = _____ km

⑱ 55 mm = _____ cm   ⑲ 371 cm = _____ m

⑳ 105 m = _____ km   ㉑ 0.8 m = _____ cm

> **Simple Conversion**
>
> Big unit ⟶ × Small unit
> Big unit ⟵ ÷ Small unit
>
> e.g. 3.2 km = 3200 m
>   └─ × 1000 ─┘

Look at the picture. Solve the problems.

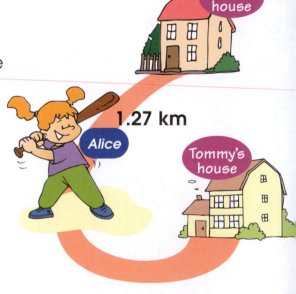

㉒ The distance between Alice's house and the baseball field is _____ m.

㉓ The distance from the baseball field to Tommy's house is half the distance between the baseball field and Alice's house. The distance from the baseball field to Tommy's house is _____ m.

㉔ Alice leaves her house and goes to Tommy's house passing through the baseball field. She has to travel _____ m in all.

Canadian Curriculum MathSmart (Grade 6)   ISBN: 978-1-927042-15-1

Look at Andrew's record. Help him complete the table. Then answer the questions.

㉕

Race	Distance	Time	Speed
1	700 km	2 h	= (km/h)
2	347 000 m	1 h	= (km/h)
3		1.2 h	345 km/h
4		1.5 h	354 km/h

Speed = $\dfrac{\text{Distance}}{\text{Time}}$

e.g. Travelling 150 km in 2 h.
Speed:
150 ÷ 2 = 75 (km/h)

㉖ In which race did Andrew drive at the highest speed?

_____

㉗ How many more kilometres will be covered in 1 hour if Andrew drives at the speed in Race 1 instead of the speed in Race 3?

_____

㉘ If it takes Andrew only 1 hour to complete Race 3, what will his speed be?

_____

㉙ If Ted walks at a speed of 4 m/s to the race course, a distance of 2160 m, how long will it take him to reach there?

_____

㉚ If Ted starts walking to the race course at 11:58 a.m., what time will he reach the race course?

_____

For question ㉙, use division to find the answer.

Time = $\dfrac{\text{Distance}}{\text{Speed}}$

A C T I V I T Y

Look at the picture. What is the distance between the turtle and the snail after 2 minutes?

0.15 m/s   0.01 m/s

100 m

_____

WORDS TO LEARN

Perimeter – the distance around the outside of a shape
Area – the number of square units a surface covers

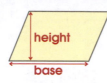

Area of a parallelogram = base x height

Area of a triangle = base x height ÷ 2

Look at the shapes. Complete the table and answer the questions.

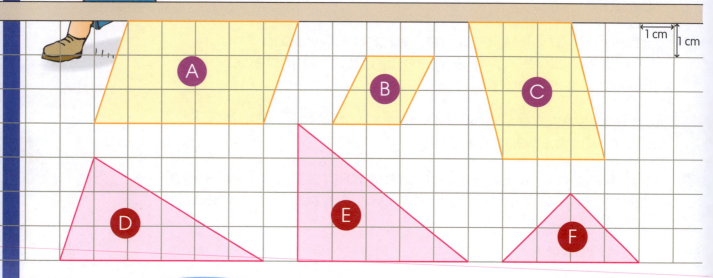

①

	Base	Height	Area
A			
B			
C			
D			
E			
F			

② Is the product of the base and height of a parallelogram the same as its area?

_____

③ Is half of the product of the base and height of a triangle the same as its area?

_____

ISBN: 978-1-927042-15-1

See how Jimmy cuts a parallelogram. Then find the base, height, area, and perimeter of each of the parallelograms.

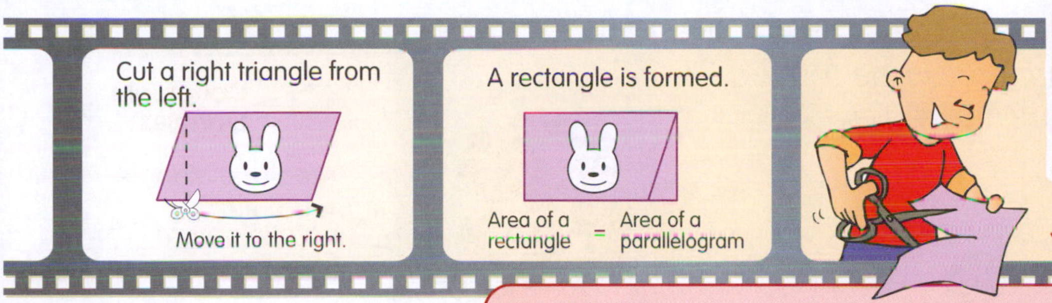

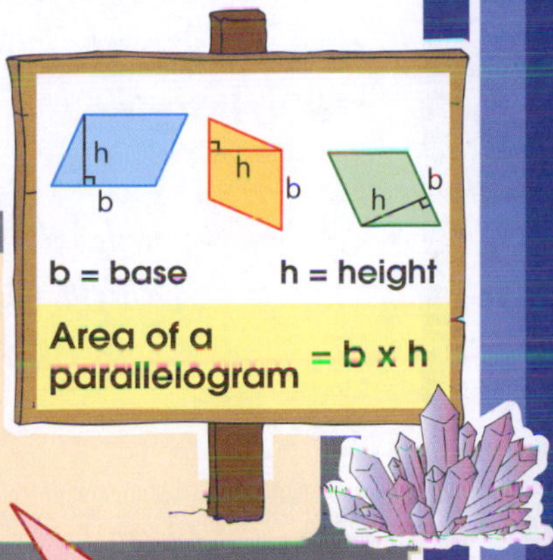

Cut a right triangle from the left.

Move it to the right.

A rectangle is formed.

Area of a rectangle = Area of a parallelogram

b = base   h = height

Area of a parallelogram = b x h

④

Find the perimeter of a parallelogram by adding the 4 sides.

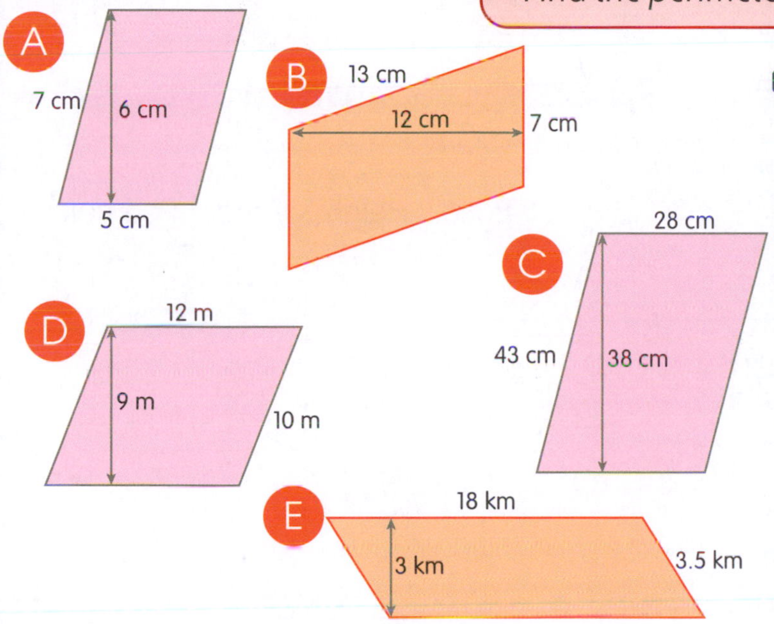

A   7 cm   6 cm   5 cm

B   13 cm   12 cm   7 cm

C   28 cm   43 cm   38 cm

D   12 m   9 m   10 m

E   18 km   3 km   3.5 km

	Base	Height	Area	Perimeter
A				
B				
C				
D				
E				

Draw the parallelograms on the grid as specified. Then colour them.

⑤

The green parallelogram has a base of 6 cm and a height of 5 cm. The area of the red parallelogram is 9 cm².

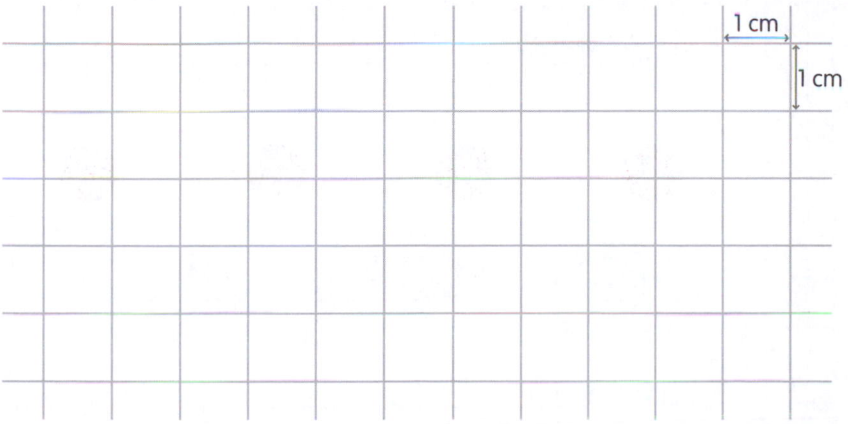

1 cm

1 cm

ISBN: 978-1-927042-15-1

Read what Karen says. Then find the base, height, area, and perimeter of each of the triangles.

A parallelogram can be formed by 2 congruent triangles.

Congruent triangles

Area of a triangle = Area of a parallelogram ÷ 2 = b x h ÷ 2

⑥

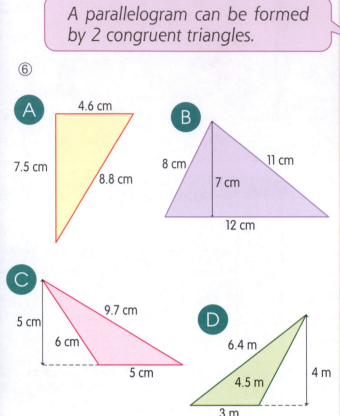

A 4.6 cm 7.5 cm 8.8 cm

B 8 cm 11 cm 7 cm 12 cm

C 9.7 cm 5 cm 6 cm 5 cm

D 6.4 m 4.5 m 4 m 3 m

	Base	Height	Area	Perimeter
A				
B				
C				
D				

Look at the triangles in each group. Put the letters in order. Start with the one that has the greatest area.

If the bases of the triangles are the same, the one with the greatest height has the greatest area.

⑦

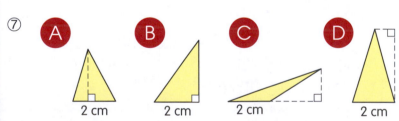

A 2 cm   B 2 cm   C 2 cm   D 2 cm

The order: _____

⑧

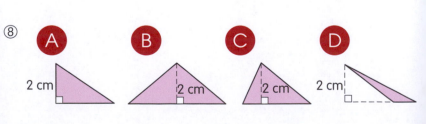

A 2 cm   B 2 cm   C 2 cm   D 2 cm

The order: _____

Canadian Curriculum MathSmart (Grade 6)   ISBN: 978-1-927042-15-1

Draw 3 different triangles, each with an area of 12 cm².

⑨

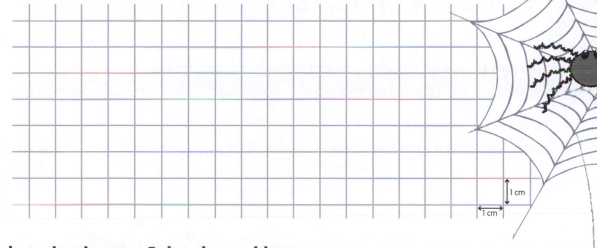

1 cm
1 cm

Look at the shapes. Solve the problems.

⑩ If the area of the parallelogram is 39 cm², what is its base?

_____ cm

⑪ If the base of the triangle is 2 times its height, what is its area?

_____ cm²

⑫ If Speedy the Spider wants to get the greatest triangle from the cardboard, what is the area of that triangle?

_____ cm²

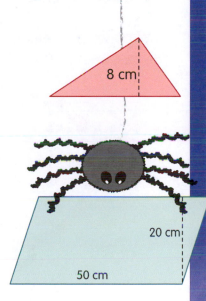

3 cm

8 cm

20 cm

50 cm

ACTIVITY

Find the area of the coloured part.

12 cm

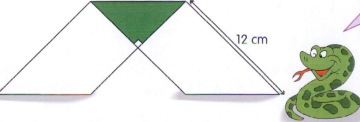

The area of each parallelogram is 96 cm².

_____ cm²

ISBN: 978-1-927042-15-1

7

8 2-D Shapes and 3-D Figures

WORDS TO LEARN

Line of symmetry – a line that cuts a shape into matching halves

Rotational symmetry – a figure has rotational symmetry if it fits on itself within a complete rotation

Order of rotational symmetry – the number of times the figure fits on itself in one complete rotation

This windmill has the rotational symmetry of order 4.

Net – a 2-D shape which can be folded into a 3-D figure

Complete each shape with the given lines of symmetry (dotted lines). Then draw the missing lines of symmetry.

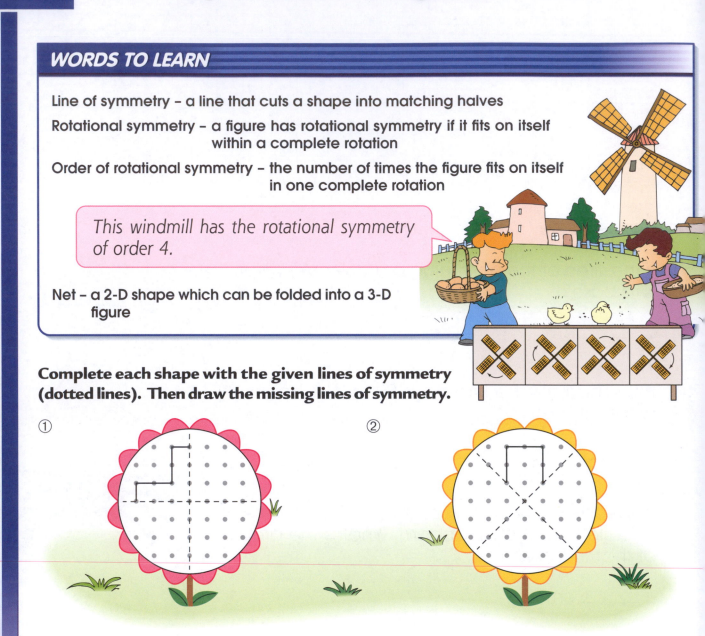

① ②

Add three squares to each shape to make it symmetrical. Then draw the line(s) of symmetry.

③

a. b. c.

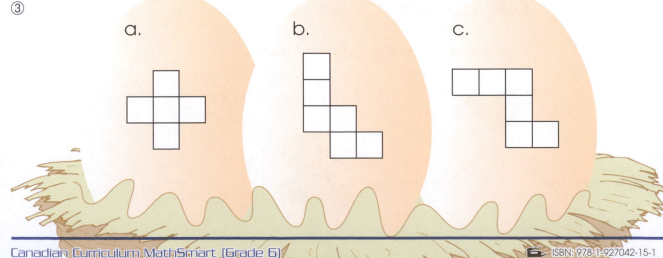

ISBN: 978-1-927042-15-1

Help the clown write the order of rotational symmetry for each shape on the line.

④

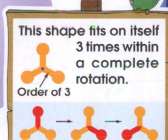

This shape fits on itself 3 times within a complete rotation.

Order of 3

Use a protractor and a ruler to construct the shapes. Then label them with the letters.

⑤

A A triangle with no rotational symmetry

B A triangle with angles of 45°, 45°, and 90°

C A rectangle with sides of 6 cm and 3 cm, and can be cut into 8 identical squares

D A parallelogram with a base of 6 cm and a height of 5 cm, and can be cut into 5 identical parallelograms

ISBN: 978-1-927042-15-1

Draw a congruent figure for each shape.

⑥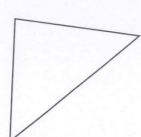

⑦

Fill in the blanks with numbers to complete what Joseph says. Then help him draw the missing parts of each net.

⑧

A rectangular pyramid 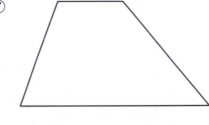 has _____ rectangular face(s) and _____ triangular face(s).

A hexagonal prism has _____ hexagonal face(s) and _____ rectangular face(s).

⑨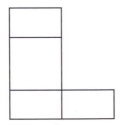

Rectangular Prism   Triangular Pyramid   Pentagonal Prism

Check ✔ the correct letters.

⑩ Which quadrilaterals have 2 pairs of parallel sides?

(A) Square   (B) Trapezoid   (C) Rhombus

⑪ Which triangle has exactly 2 equal sides?

(A) Equilateral   (B) Scalene   (C) Isosceles

⑫ Which shapes have no right angles?

(A) Rhombus   (B) Rectangle   (C) Parallelogram

Draw the models on the isometric dot paper.

⑬

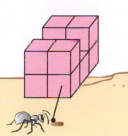  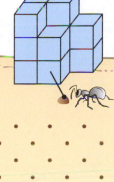

A C T I V I T Y

Are the triangles similar? Measure the angles of each triangle. Then explain.

_____

_____

ISBN: 978-1-927042-15-1

Midway Test

Use the property of multiplication to find the answers. (2 marks)

① $9 \times (8 + 7)$

$= 9 \times \underline{\hspace{1cm}} + 9 \times \underline{\hspace{1cm}}$

$= \underline{\hspace{1cm}} + \underline{\hspace{1cm}}$

$= \underline{\hspace{1cm}}$

② $(116 - 29) \times 3$

$= 116 \times \underline{\hspace{1cm}} - 29 \times \underline{\hspace{1cm}}$

$= \underline{\hspace{1cm}} - \underline{\hspace{1cm}}$

$= \underline{\hspace{1cm}}$

Find the answers. (8 marks)

③ $34 \div (19 - 2)$

$=$

④ $18 + 8 \times 10$

$=$

⑤ $22 \times 5 - 60$

$=$

⑥ $(43 + 7) \div 2$

$=$

Write the first eight multiples of each pair of numbers. Then find their common multiple(s) and L.C.M. (8 marks)

⑦ **7** : _____ , _____ , _____ , _____ , _____ , _____ , _____ , _____

 8 : _____ , _____ , _____ , _____ , _____ , _____ , _____ , _____

Common multiple(s) : _____   L.C.M. : _____

⑧ **6** : _____ , _____ , _____ , _____ , _____ , _____ , _____ , _____

 9 : _____ , _____ , _____ , _____ , _____ , _____ , _____ , _____

Common multiple(s) : _____   L.C.M. : _____

ISBN: 978-1-927042-15-1

Find the answers. (14 marks)

⑨

$$25\overline{)9150}$$

⑩

$$37\overline{)2833}$$

⑪

$$\begin{array}{r} 782 \\ \times \quad 32 \\ \hline \end{array}$$

⑫ 695 x 47 = _____

⑬ 8001 ÷ 19 = _____

⑭ 29 x 163 = _____

⑮ 5107 ÷ 23 = _____

Look at the map. Then fill in the blanks. (6 marks)

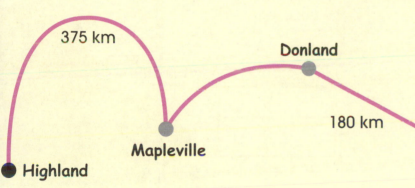

375 km

Donland

Mapleville

180 km

Highland

Welcome to
Sunville

⑯ It takes the train 2 h to travel from Sunville to Donland. What is the travelling speed?

_____

⑰ If the train keeps the above speed and travels from Donland to Mapleville in 2.5 h, what is the distance between these two cities?

_____

⑱ The train leaves Mapleville at a speed of 75 km/h at 13:05. What time will it arrive at Highland?

_____

Midway Test

Find the factors of the numbers in each group. Then find their common factor(s) and G.C.F. (8 marks)

⑲

20 : _____

32 : _____

Common factors : _____

G.C.F. : _____

⑳

18 : _____

24 : _____

Common factors : _____

G.C.F. : _____

Look at the weather forecast. Answer the questions. (3 marks)

㉑ What is the temperature in Halifax today?

_____

㉒ Is the temperature in Edmonton higher than that in Toronto today?

_____

㉓ Which day in Toronto has a higher temperature?

_____

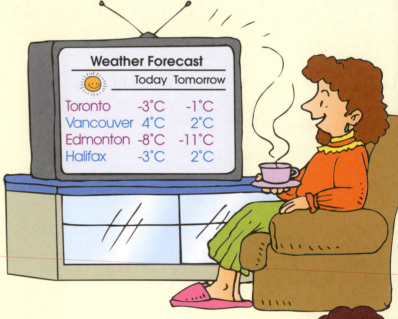

Weather Forecast

	Today	Tomorrow
Toronto	-3°C	-1°C
Vancouver	4°C	2°C
Edmonton	-8°C	-11°C
Halifax	-3°C	2°C

Help George draw the shapes. (4 marks)

㉔ A triangle with 3 lines of symmetry

㉕ A parallelogram with a base of 5 cm and a height of 3 cm

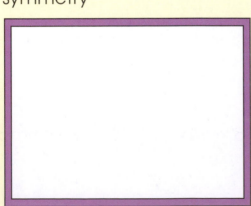

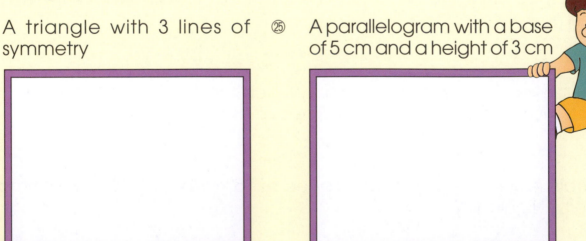

ISBN: 978-1-927042-15-1

Write each number as a product of prime factors. Then find the L.C.M. and G.C.F. of each pair of numbers. (㉖ 6 marks, ㉗ – ㉚ 8 marks)

㉖ a. 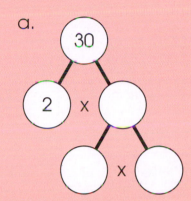 b. 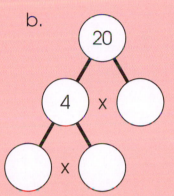 c.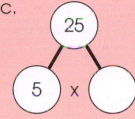

30 = _____   20 = _____   25 = _____

㉗   The G.C.F. of 20 and 30 is _____ .

㉘   The G.C.F. of 25 and 30 is _____ .

㉙   The L.C.M. of 20 and 30 is _____ .

㉚   The L.C.M. of 20 and 25 is _____ .

Write the order of rotational symmetry for each shape. (2 marks)

㉛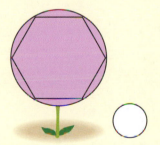

㉜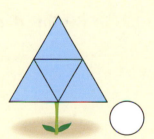

Find the answers. (4 marks)

㉝   42 066 – 6997 = _____

㉞   395 + 285 + 98 + 122 = _____

㉟   90 303 – 2455 = _____

㊱   898 + 302 + 788 + 477 = _____

ISBN: 978-1-927042-15-1

Find the area and the perimeter of each shape. (8 marks)

③⑦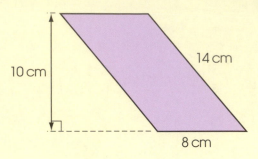

Area = _____

Perimeter = _____

③⑧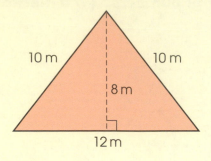

Area = _____

Perimeter = _____

Draw a parallelogram and a triangle each with an area of 16 cm². (2 marks)

③⑨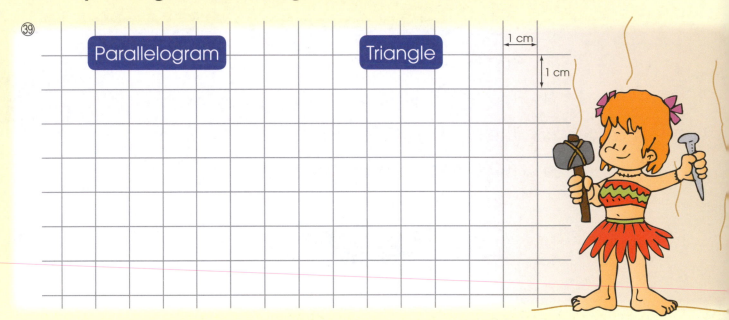

Draw the models of the interlocking cubes. (4 marks)

④⓪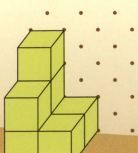

④①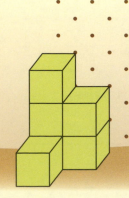

ISBN: 978-1-927042-15-1

Complete each symmetrical shape with the help of the lines of symmetry (red lines). Then draw one congruent figure for each shape. (4 marks)

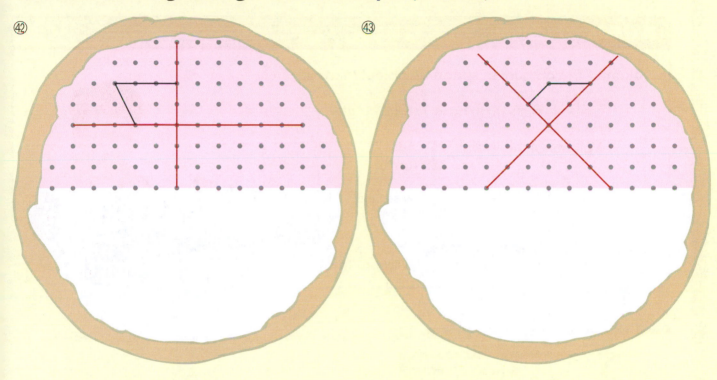

㊷

㊸

Solve the problems. (9 marks)

$13

㊹ How much will Uncle Philip earn from selling 927 pizzas?

㊺ Uncle Philip expects to earn $13 000 next month. If he is going to earn $4662 less than expected, how much will he earn next month?

㊻ If 3348 pizzas are sold in March, how many pizzas are sold in a day on average?

Score

100

ISBN: 978-1-927042-15-1

9 Volume and Mass

WORDS TO LEARN

Volume – the amount of space an object takes up

> **Volume of a Prism: Base Area x Height**

Volume of the Prism: 25 x 14
= 350 (cm^3)

Base area:
25 cm^2

14 cm

Mass – units for measuring mass:
Kilogram (kg), Gram (g), Milligram (mg)

Find the volume of each prism.

Base area: 18 m^2

A   2 m

Base area: 96 cm^2

B   8 cm

Base area:
85 cm^2

C   3 cm

Base area: 28 cm^2

D   15 cm

Base area:
33 cm^2

E   9 cm

① Volume

A

B

C

D

E

Help Joey the Cat solve the problems.

② A box measures 8 cm by 9 cm by
4.5 cm. What is its volume?
_____ cm^3

③ What is the volume of each solid?

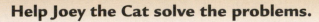

10 cm   10 cm
15 cm
10 cm   5 cm

7 cm   4 cm   4 cm   7 cm
4 cm   5 cm

_____ cm^3 _____ cm^3

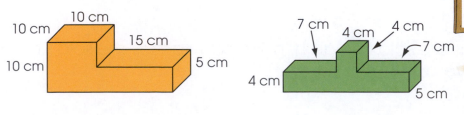

Volume of a Prism:
Base Area x Height

ISBN: 978-1-927042-15-1

Fill in the blanks.

④ 9 kg + 8 g = _____ g

⑤ 2510 g + 1880 g = _____ kg

⑥ 6 g + 145 mg = _____ mg

⑦ 33 mg + 945 mg = _____ g

⑧ 8 g + 9.24 g = _____ mg

⑨ 0.65 kg + 250 g = _____ kg

⑩ 1.2 kg + 60 g = _____ g

⑪ 1726 mg + 0.274 g = _____ g

Read what Tim says. Find the weights of the aliens and write the answers in grams on their T-shirts. Then answer the questions.

> George is 500 g less than 8 kg. The total weight of George and Louis is 15.5 kg. If Wayne gains 5 mg, he will weigh 1 g. Ted is 5 times as heavy as Wayne. Richard is 2.9 kg lighter than Louis. Bob is 0.225 g heavier than Ted.

⑫

George   Louis   Wayne   Richard   Bob   Ted

⑬ Who is the heaviest? _____

⑭ Who is the lightest? _____

ACTIVITY

Read what Ray says. Help him solve the problem.

> The total weight of 3 balls and myself is 886 g. If I weigh 400 000 mg, how much does each ball weigh?

_____ g

10 Operations with Decimals

WORDS TO LEARN

Decimal – a numeral containing a decimal point with the value of digits to the right of the decimal point being less than 1

The dog weighs about 9.19 kg.

I weigh 9 and 186 thousandths kilograms.

Ones Hundredths
Tenths Thousandths

9 . 1 8 6 kg

Expanded form:
$9.186 = 9 + 0.1 + 0.08 + 0.006$

Write the decimals in expanded form and in words.

① **45.619** In expanded form: _____

In words: _____

② **60.202** In expanded form: _____

In words: _____

Find the answers.

③
```
   6 . 8
-  2 . 5 4 9
_____
```

④
```
   3 . 1 7 5
+  0 . 8 5 6
_____
```

⑤
```
   4 . 0 1 7
-  3 . 8 5
_____
```

⑥ $9.14 + 2.889 =$ _____   ⑦ $3.46 - 0.875 =$ _____

⑧ $4.06 - 3.451 =$ _____   ⑨ $7.07 + 1.864 =$ _____

⑩ If Susan weighs 28.64 kg, her cat weighs _____ kg.

⑪ If Susan's cat gains 0.524 kg, it will weigh _____ kg.

32.887 kg

Canadian Curriculum MathSmart (Grade 6)   ISBN: 978-1-927042-15-1

Find the products or quotients mentally.

⑫ 2.623 x 100 = ______ ⑬ 3.88 ÷ 10 = ______

⑭ 89.4 ÷ 100 = ______ ⑮ 0.767 x 100 = ______

⑯ 5.051 x 10 = ______ ⑰ 305.4 ÷ 100 = ______

⑱ 6.25 ÷ 100 = ______ ⑲ 1 ÷ 1000 = ______

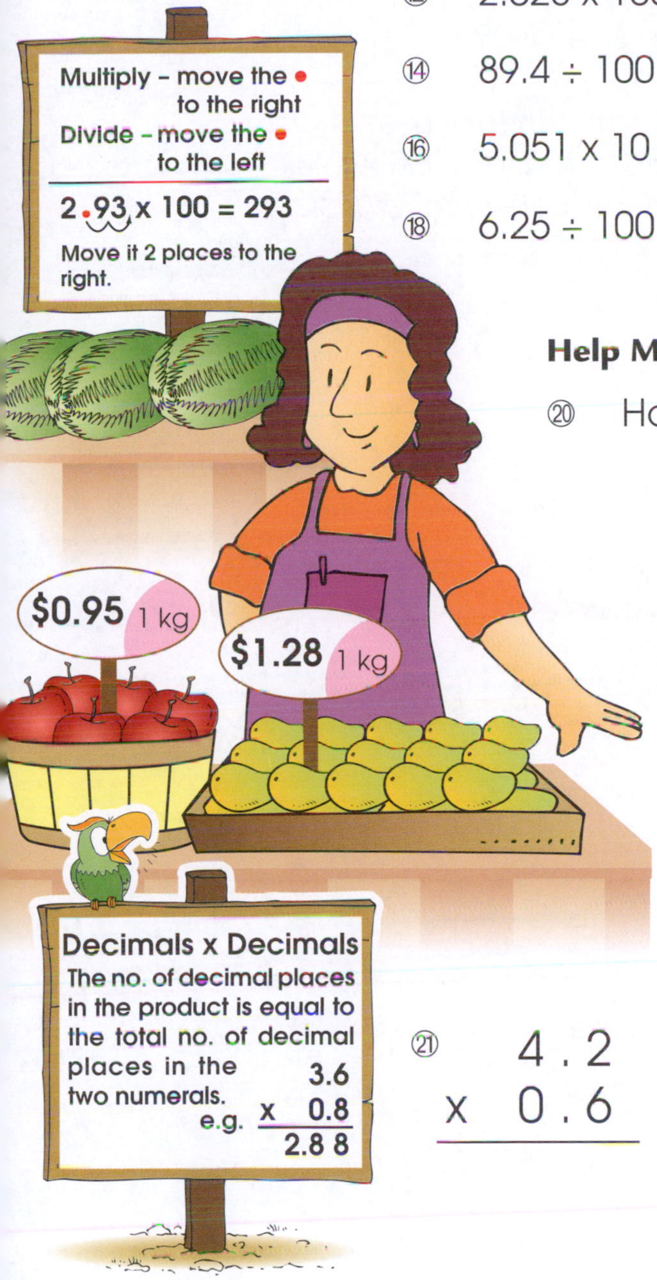

Multiply – move the • to the right
Divide – move the • to the left
2.93 x 100 = 293
Move it 2 places to the right.
$0.95 1 kg
$1.28 1 kg
Decimals x Decimals
The no. of decimal places in the product is equal to the total no. of decimal places in the two numerals.
e.g. 3.6 x 0.8 = 2.88

Help Mrs. Martin solve the problems.

⑳ How much do 2.6 kg of apples cost?

```
     0 . 9 5   ← 2 decimal places
x      2 . 6   ← 1 decimal place
    ---------
       5 7 0
     1 9 0 0
    ---------
     □.□ □ □   ← 3 decimal places
```

2.6 kg of apples cost $ ______ .

㉑ 4.2 x 0.6

㉒ 3.25 x 0.8

㉓ 4.668 x 3

㉔ 6.27 x 1.8 = ______ ㉕ 3.5 x 2.66 = ______

㉖ 4.15 x 6.3 = ______ ㉗ 10.2 x 3.17 = ______

㉘ 8.06 x 1.4 = ______ ㉙ 2.19 x 8.5 = ______

㉚ 3.8 kg of apples cost $ ______ (correct to 1 decimal place).

㉛ 4.7 kg of mangoes cost $ ______ (correct to 2 decimal places).

㉜ 1.5 kg of mangoes cost $ ______ (correct to 2 decimal places).

ISBN: 978-1-927042-15-1

Follow Elaine's method to do the division.

㉝ Elaine wants to cut a 0.75-m long ribbon into strips of 0.15 m each. How many strips can she get?

$$0.75 \div 0.15 = \frac{0.75}{0.15}$$

$$= \frac{0.75 \times 100}{0.15 \times 100}$$

Multiply the dividend and the divisor by 10, 100, or 1000 to make the divisor a whole number first.

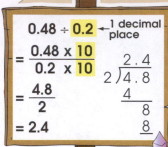

$$= \frac{}{15}$$

$$15 \overline{)7\,5}$$

$$= \underline{}$$

$$\underline{}$$

She can get _____ strips.

㉞ $32.4 \div 0.4$

$$= \frac{32.4 \times }{0.4 \times }$$

$$4\overline{)}$$

$$= \frac{}{4}$$

$$= \underline{}$$

㉟ $1.6 \div 0.08$

$$= \frac{1.6 \times }{0.08 \times }$$

$$8\overline{)}$$

$$= \frac{}{8}$$

$$= \underline{}$$

㊱ $8.85 \div 0.05 =$ _____

㊲ $3.45 \div 0.23 =$ _____

㊳ $0.221 \div 1.3 =$ _____

㊴ $29.45 \div 1.9 =$ _____

㊵ $16.74 \div 2.7 =$ _____

㊶ $12.18 \div 0.87 =$ _____

㊷ Each roll of ribbon costs $0.95. How many rolls of ribbon can Tony buy with $17.10?

_____ rolls of ribbon

㊸ 1.5 m of ribbon is needed to tie a gift box. How many gift boxes can be tied with 13.5 m of ribbon?

_____ gift boxes

ISBN: 978-1-927042-15-1

Find the answers.

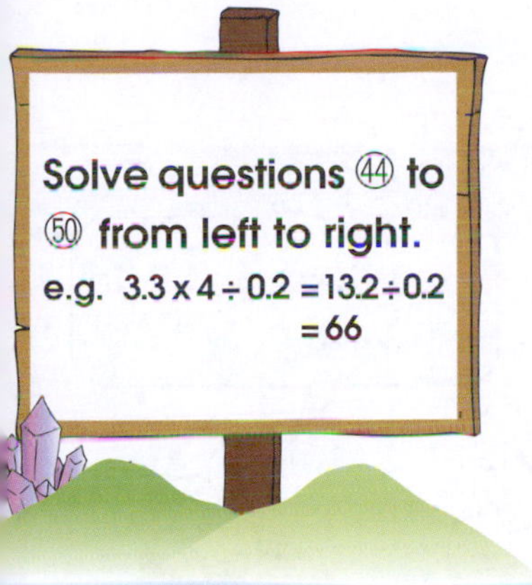
Solve questions ㊹ to ㊿ from left to right.
e.g. 3.3 x 4 ÷ 0.2 = 13.2 ÷ 0.2
= 66

㊹ 3.2 + 1.4 – 0.58 = ______

㊺ 6.4 ÷ 0.4 x 1.3 = ______

㊻ 3.84 – 1.765 + 2.339 = ______

㊼ 6.447 + 1.385 – 2.608 = ______

㊽ 3.5 x 1.9 ÷ 0.5 = ______

㊾ 8.91 ÷ 2.7 x 1.44 = ______

㊿ 17.8 x 4.2 ÷ 2.8 = ______

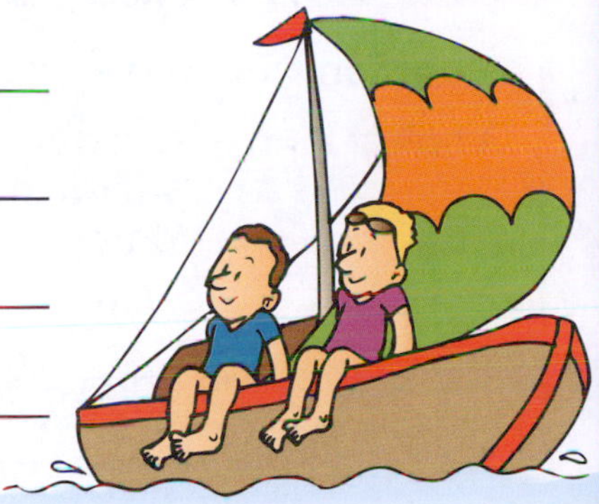

Solve the problems.

(51) A boat covered a distance of 32.8 km in 1 h. It will cover ________ km in 2.4 h.

(52) Peter travelled 3.258 km on Monday and 4.165 km on Tuesday. He travelled ________ km in the past two days.

(53) Sister Shark weighs 68.259 kg. If Sister Shark is 6.84 kg lighter than Brother Shark, Brother Shark weighs ________ kg.

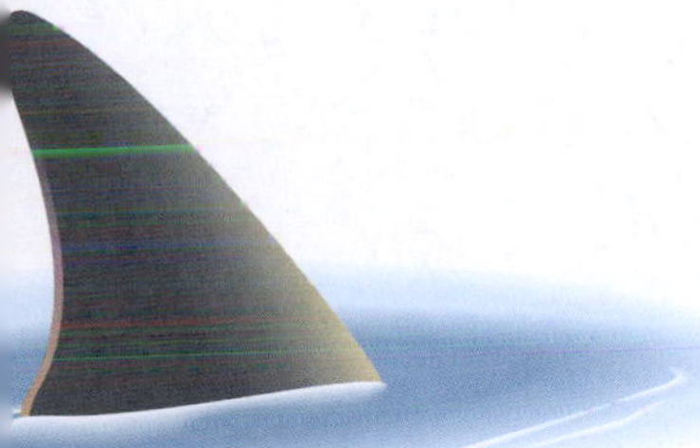

(54) Brother Shark can swim 96.6 km in 1.5 h. He can travel ________ km in 1 h.

(55) Sister Shark is 0.87 m long. If Brother Shark is 1.2 times as long as Sister Shark, he is ________ m long.

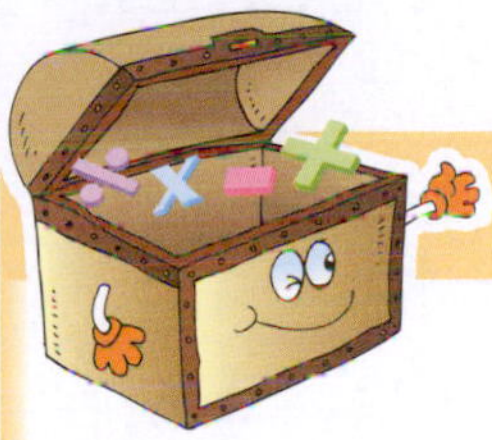

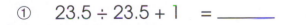

ACTIVITY

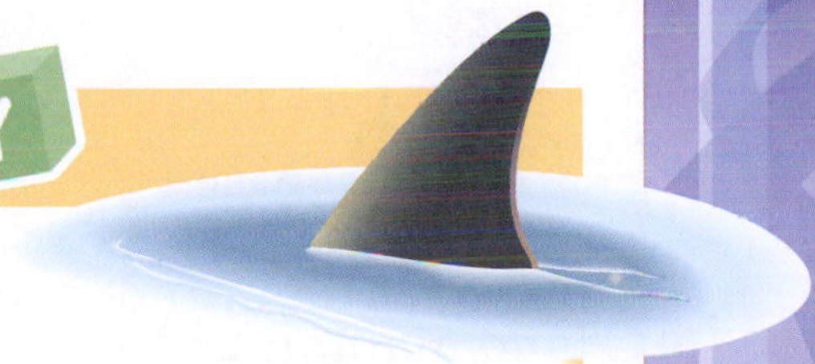

Work out the answers mentally.

① 23.5 ÷ 23.5 + 1 = ______

② 12.14 ÷ 2 x 2 = ______

③ 382.4 x 0 + 5.3 = ______

④ 1 x 8.86 ÷ 1 = ______

⑤ 6.65 – 6.65 + 3.4 = ______

⑥ 8.04 x 1 – 8.04 = ______

ISBN: 978-1-927042-15-1

11 Operations with Fractions

WORDS TO LEARN

Equivalent fractions – fractions that represent the same value

Simplest form – a fraction in which the numerator and denominator have only 1 as their common factor

$\frac{1}{2}$ and $\frac{2}{4}$ are equivalent fractions. $\frac{1}{2}$ is a fraction in simplest form.

I am as strong as you.

Change the improper fractions into mixed numbers and mixed numbers into improper fractions.

① $\frac{11}{3}$ = _____

② $4\frac{3}{7}$ = _____

③ $1\frac{4}{5}$ = _____

④ $2\frac{3}{5}$ = _____

⑤ $\frac{13}{9}$ = _____

⑥ $\frac{19}{6}$ = _____

⑦ $1\frac{3}{4}$ = _____

⑧ $\frac{18}{7}$ = _____

⑨ $3\frac{1}{8}$ = _____

⑩ $6\frac{1}{2}$ = _____

⑪ $2\frac{1}{2}$ = _____

⑫ $\frac{25}{9}$ = _____

Improper fraction $\xrightarrow{\div}{\underset{\times}{\longleftarrow}}$ Mixed number

$\frac{7}{5}$ = 7 ÷ 5 = $1\frac{2}{5}$

$3\frac{1}{4}$ = $\frac{3 \times 4 + 1}{4}$ = $\frac{13}{4}$

Compare the fractions. Put ">" or "<" in the circles.

⑬ $\frac{5}{6}$ ◯ $\frac{7}{18}$

⑭ $\frac{4}{15}$ ◯ $\frac{2}{3}$

⑮ $2\frac{2}{5}$ ◯ $2\frac{7}{15}$

⑯ $5\frac{1}{2}$ ◯ $5\frac{3}{8}$

⑰ $\frac{9}{4}$ ◯ $2\frac{5}{8}$

⑱ $1\frac{1}{3}$ ◯ $\frac{11}{6}$

⑲ $1\frac{4}{7}$ ◯ $\frac{29}{21}$

⑳ $\frac{13}{9}$ ◯ $1\frac{1}{3}$

To compare fractions, find a common denominator and compare the numerators.

$\frac{8}{18} \rightarrow \frac{4}{9}$ ❯ $\frac{7}{18}$ Common denominator: 18

Canadian Curriculum MathSmart (Grade 6)   ISBN: 978-1-927042-15-1

Do the addition or subtraction. Write the answers in simplest form.

When the denominators are the same, add or subtract only the numerators. Write the fraction in simplest form.

(21)

$$\frac{2}{9} + \frac{1}{9} = \frac{}{9} = \frac{}{3}$$

(22)

$$\frac{5}{6} - \frac{1}{6} = \frac{}{6} = \frac{}{3}$$

(23) $\frac{11}{12} - \frac{5}{12} = \underline{\hspace{1cm}} = \underline{\hspace{1cm}}$

(24) $\frac{6}{7} + \frac{1}{7} = \underline{\hspace{1cm}} = \underline{\hspace{1cm}}$

(25) $\frac{8}{15} + \frac{2}{15} = \underline{\hspace{1cm}} = \underline{\hspace{1cm}}$

(26) $\frac{19}{20} - \frac{11}{20} = \underline{\hspace{1cm}} = \underline{\hspace{1cm}}$

(27) $\frac{3}{10} + \frac{9}{10} = \underline{\hspace{1cm}} = \underline{\hspace{1cm}}$

(28) $\frac{17}{18} - \frac{1}{18} = \underline{\hspace{1cm}} = \underline{\hspace{1cm}}$

Solve the problems. Write the answers in simplest form.

(29) The children spent $\frac{5}{12}$ h playing volleyball and $\frac{11}{12}$ h playing beach ball. How much time did the children spend playing ball games?

_____ h

(30) It took Jason $\frac{5}{8}$ h to pick 100 shells; it took Peter $\frac{7}{8}$ h. How much longer did it take Peter than Jason?

_____ h

(31) $\frac{7}{15}$ of the children wore yellow T-shirts and $\frac{2}{15}$ of the children wore green T-shirts. What fraction of the children wore either yellow or green T-shirts?

_____ of the children

Look at the coloured parts of each diagram. Fill in the blanks with fractions to complete the addition and subtraction sentences.

③②

③③

_____ + _____ = _____   _____ – _____ = _____

③④

③⑤

_____ + _____ = _____   _____ – _____ = _____

Write the answers in simplest form.

③⑥ $\dfrac{2}{5} - \dfrac{1}{10}$

$= \dfrac{}{10} - \dfrac{1}{10}$

$= \dfrac{}{10}$

$= \underline{}$

③⑦ $\dfrac{4}{7} + \dfrac{3}{14}$

$= \dfrac{}{14} + \dfrac{3}{14}$

$= \dfrac{}{14}$

> **To add /subtract fractions with different denominators:**
>
> · Write equivalent fractions with a common denominator.
> · Add/subtract the numerators.
> · Write the answers in simplest form.

③⑧ $\dfrac{1}{3} + \dfrac{7}{24} = \underline{}$

③⑨ $\dfrac{17}{20} - \dfrac{1}{5} = \underline{}$

④⓪ $\dfrac{3}{4} + \dfrac{1}{12} = \underline{}$

④① $\dfrac{3}{5} - \dfrac{1}{3} = \underline{}$

④② $\dfrac{9}{10} - \dfrac{1}{2} = \underline{}$

④③ $\dfrac{1}{15} + \dfrac{4}{5} = \underline{}$

④④ $\dfrac{7}{16} - \dfrac{1}{4} = \underline{}$

④⑤ $\dfrac{3}{4} + \dfrac{1}{20} = \underline{}$

④⑥ $\dfrac{7}{8} - \dfrac{5}{16} = \underline{}$

④⑦ $\dfrac{11}{24} - \dfrac{1}{3} = \underline{}$

$\dfrac{4}{15} + \dfrac{1}{3}$ Common denominator: 15

$= \dfrac{4}{15} + \dfrac{5}{15}$

$= \dfrac{9}{15}$ ← Add the numerators.

$= \dfrac{3}{5}$ ← Write the answer in simplest form.

ISBN: 978-1-927042-15-1

Brian went camping with his family. Help him solve the problems. Write the answers in simplest form.

48 Brian and his family travelled $\frac{5}{6}$ h and walked $\frac{1}{3}$ h from their house to the campsite. How much time did it take them in all?

It took them _____ h in all.

49 Brian and his sister, Sara, went to get some water. If Brian carried $\frac{17}{20}$ of a pail of water and Sara carried $\frac{3}{4}$ of a pail of water, how much more water did Brian carry than Sara?

Brian carried _____ more of a pail of water than Sara.

50 It took Brian's father, Mr. Prem, $\frac{9}{10}$ h to build the first tent and $\frac{1}{5}$ h to build the second tent. How much time did he spend building the tents?

He spent _____ h building the tents.

ACTIVITY

Solve the problem.

Brian has a jug of juice. If he drinks $\frac{2}{5}$ L every day, how many days will the jug of juice last?

No. of Days	1	2		
Amount of Juice Consumed (L)	$\frac{2}{5}$	$\frac{4}{5}$		

The jug of juice will last _____ days.

12 Fractions, Decimals, and Percents

WORDS TO LEARN

Percent (%) – represents a part of 100 or out of 100

e.g.   40% means 40 out of 100.

$\div 100$

A percent → A fraction or decimal

$\times 100$

e.g. $57\% = 57 \div 100 = \dfrac{57}{100} = 0.57$

$\dfrac{29}{100} = \dfrac{29}{100} \times 100\% = 0.29 \times 100\% = 29\%$

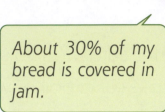

About 30% of my bread is covered in jam.

Rewrite as a percent (%).

① Twenty-five percent _____

② Fifty percent _____

③ 41 out of 100 _____

④ 7 out of 100 _____

⑤ 80 out of 100 _____

⑥ Two percent _____

⑦ Thirty percent _____

⑧ 92 out of 100 _____

Colour each 100-square grid to match each percent.

⑨ 65%   ⑩ 8%   ⑪ 90%

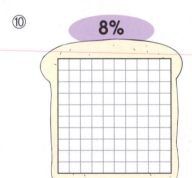

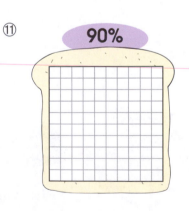

Write each coloured part as a fraction, decimal, and percent.

⑫
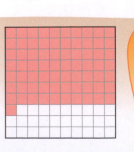

_____
_____
_____

⑬

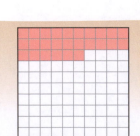

_____
_____
_____

ISBN: 978-1-927042-15-1

Rewrite as percents.

⑭ $\dfrac{13}{100} =$ _____

⑮ $\dfrac{57}{100} =$ _____

⑯ $\dfrac{8}{100} =$ _____

⑰ $\dfrac{7}{20} = \dfrac{}{100} =$ _____

⑱ $\dfrac{3}{4} = \dfrac{}{100} =$ _____

⑲ $3\dfrac{8}{25} = 3\dfrac{}{100} =$ _____

⑳ $4\dfrac{1}{2} = 4\dfrac{}{100} =$ _____

㉑ $1\dfrac{9}{10} =$ _____ $=$ _____

㉒ $\dfrac{11}{50} =$ _____ $=$ _____

㉓ $2\dfrac{1}{4} =$ _____ $=$ _____

㉔ $1\dfrac{17}{20} =$ _____ $=$ _____

Write a fraction as a percent:

$\dfrac{2}{5} = \dfrac{40}{100}$

$= 40\%$

Write an equivalent fraction using 100 as the denominator.

Rewrite as fractions in simplest form.

㉕ 38% _____

㉖ 60% _____

㉗ 8% _____

㉘ 40% _____

㉙ 190% _____

㉚ 250% _____

Fill in the blanks to describe the students' scores.

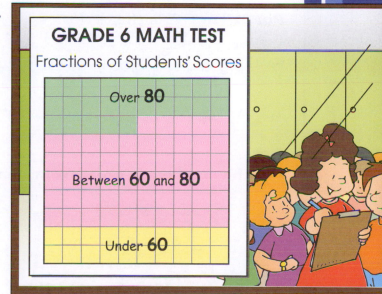

GRADE 6 MATH TEST

Fractions of Students' Scores

Over **80**

Between **60** and **80**

Under **60**

㉛ _____ % or _____ of the students got scores between 60 and 80.

㉜ _____ % or _____ of the students got scores higher than 80.

㉝ _____ % or _____ of the students got scores lower than 60.

㉞ There were 100 students;

a. _____ students got scores higher than 80.

b. _____ students got scores lower than 60.

c. _____ students got scores between 60 and 80.

ISBN: 978-1-927042-15-1

12

Write the percents as fractions with 100 as the denominator first. Then write them as decimals.

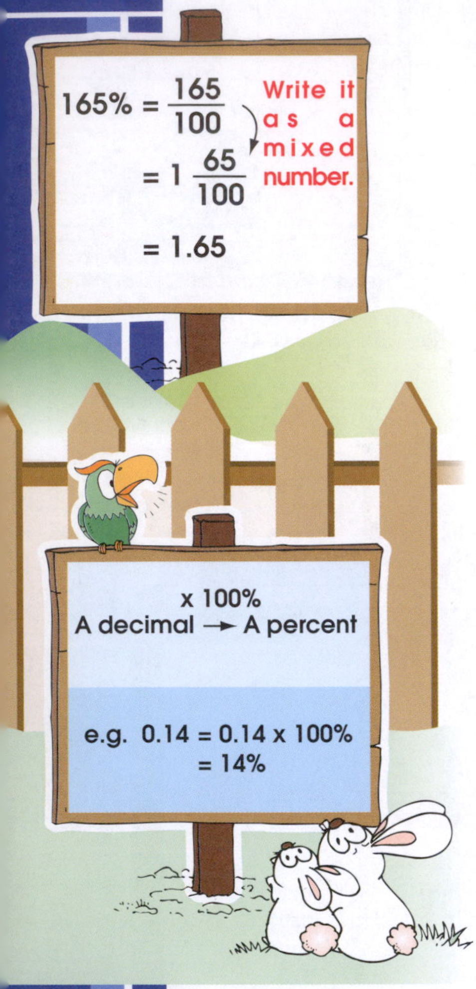

$165\% = \frac{165}{100}$
$= 1\frac{65}{100}$
$= 1.65$
Write it as a mixed number.
x 100%
A decimal → A percent
e.g. 0.14 = 0.14 x 100%
= 14%

㉟ 20% $= \frac{\quad}{100}$ = ______

㊱ 5% $= \frac{\quad}{100}$ = ______

㊲ 77% = ______ = ______

㊳ 60% = ______ = ______

㊴ 125% = ______ = ______

㊵ 190% = ______ = ______

㊶ 142% = ______ = ______

㊷ 106% = ______ = ______

Write the decimals as percents.

㊸ 0.34 = ______ %

㊹ 0.06 = ______ %

㊺ 0.8 = ______ %

㊻ 1.43 = ______ %

㊼ 1.2 = ______ %

㊽ 0.27 = ______ %

㊾ 6.04 = ______ %

㊿ 0.92 = ______ %

Put ">" or "<" in the circles.

(51) 5.6% ◯ 0.56

(52) 24% ◯ 0.024

(53) 0.11 ◯ 10%

(54) 125% ◯ 1.52

(55) 3.08 ◯ 30.8%

(56) 42% ◯ 0.042

Put the numbers in order from smallest to greatest.

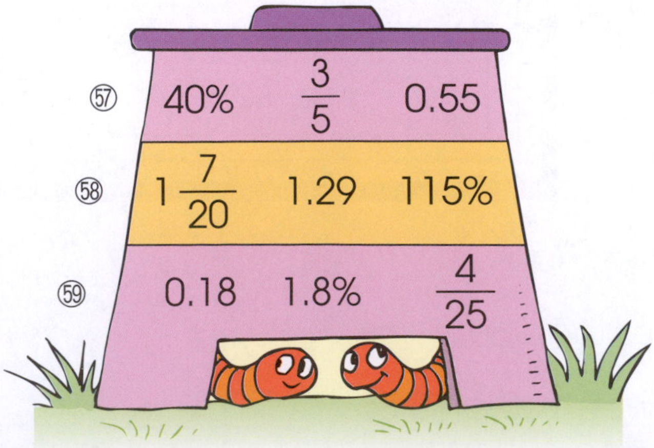

(57) 40% $\frac{3}{5}$ 0.55
(58) $1\frac{7}{20}$ 1.29 115%
(59) 0.18 1.8% $\frac{4}{25}$

(57) ______________________

(58) ______________________

(59) ______________________

ISBN: 978-1-927042-15-1

Read what Uncle John says. Help him solve the problems.

> There are 50 light bulbs on a wire. 20 of them are red, 25 yellow, and the rest blue.

60 _____ (fraction) or _____ (percent) of the light bulbs are red.

61 _____ (percent) or _____ (decimal) of the light bulbs are yellow.

62 _____ (fraction) or _____ (decimal) of the light bulbs are blue.

63 If 2 light bulbs burned out, what percent of the light bulbs burned out? _____

64 If 5 light bulbs are removed, what percent of the light bulbs are still on the wire? _____

ACTIVITY

Read the bar graph. Then answer the questions.

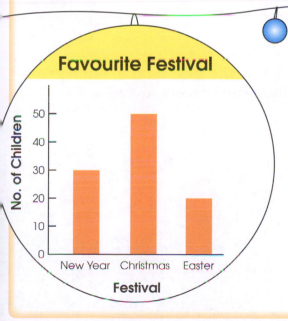

Favourite Festival

No. of Children (y-axis: 0, 10, 20, 30, 40, 50)

Festival (x-axis: New Year, Christmas, Easter)

① Which festival is the most popular?

_____

② If 100 children were asked about their favourite festivals, what percent of the children prefer

a. New Year? _____

b. Christmas? _____

c. Easter? _____

13 Rate and Ratio

WORDS TO LEARN

Rate – a comparison of two numbers with different units
e.g. $4/week, 100 km/h

Ratio – a comparison of numbers with the same unit
e.g. red apples to green apples = 3:4

A ratio can be expressed in fraction form, e.g. $3:4 = \frac{3}{4}$.

Find the cost per kilogram of each kind of fruit.

$5.88 for 3 kg

$13.12 for 4 kg

$6.96 for 8 kg

$8.70 for 5 kg

$7.49 for 7 kg

$15.72 for 6 kg

①

 $ _____ /kg $ _____ /kg

 $ _____ /kg $ _____ /kg

 $ _____ /kg    $ _____ /kg

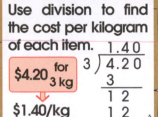

Use division to find the cost per kilogram of each item.

$4.20 for 3 kg → $1.40/kg

$$\begin{array}{r} 1.40 \\ 3\overline{)4.20} \\ \underline{3} \\ 1\,2 \\ \underline{1\,2} \end{array}$$

Which is the best deal in each group? Colour the correct answer.

② 4 for $1.12   3 for 99¢   3 for $1.35

③ 2 for $1.08   3 for $1.56   5 for $2.75

④ 5 for $4.40   2 for $1.98   3 for $2.67

Canadian Curriculum MathSmart (Grade 6)   ISBN: 978-1-927042-15-1

Look at the flying insects. Write the ratios.

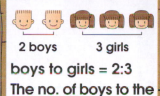

⑤ bees to butterflies = _____ : _____

⑥ dragonflies to butterflies = _____

⑦ dragonflies to bees = _____

⑧ bees to all = _____

⑨ dragonflies to all = _____

⑩ butterflies to all = _____

2 boys   3 girls

boys to girls = 2:3
The no. of boys to the no. of girls is 2 to 3.

Follow the steps to write 2 equivalent ratios for each ratio.

Multiply each term by 3.   Divide each term by 2.

x 3
2:4 = 6:12
x 3

÷ 2
2:4 = 1:2
÷ 2

Equivalent ratios can be found by multiplying or dividing each term by the same number other than 0.

1:2, 2:4, and 6:12 are equivalent ratios.

⑪ 2:3 _____ _____   ⑫ 5:4 _____ _____

⑬ 6:18 _____ _____   ⑭ 8:6 _____ _____

⑮ 28:21 _____ _____   ⑯ 4:10 _____ _____

The ratio is in simplest form if the only common factor of the terms is 1.
e.g. The ratio 3:2 is in simplest form.

Write each ratio in simplest form.

⑰ 5:10 _____   ⑱ 12:32 _____

⑲ 8:14 _____   ⑳ 9:6 _____

㉑ 12:20 _____   ㉒ 15:20 _____

㉓ 24:3 _____   ㉔ 18:8 _____

Look at the pictures that Sam has drawn. Help him write each ratio in simplest form.

㉕

a. stars to happy faces   = _____

b. hearts to happy faces   = _____

c. happy faces to all   = _____

d. hearts to all   = _____

e. stars to all   = _____

㉖

a. apples to oranges   = _____

b. oranges to pears   = _____

c. apples to pears   = _____

d. red apples to green apples   = _____

e. yellow pears to green pears   = _____

f. small oranges to big oranges   = _____

g. green apples to green pears   = _____

h. pears to all   = _____

i. oranges to all   = _____

Canadian Curriculum MathSmart (Grade 6)   ISBN: 978-1-927042-15-1

Today is Mr. Beth's birthday. His grandchildren are celebrating with him. Help the children solve the problems. Write the answers in simplest form.

㉗ What is the ratio of red balloons to blue balloons?

_____

㉘ What is the ratio of green balloons to red balloons?

_____

㉙ What is the ratio of grandsons to granddaughters?

_____

$19.35 for 3 kg

$1.68 for 3 boxes

$1.47 for 3 boxes

㉚ What is the ratio of orange juice to apple juice?   _____

㉛ What is the unit price of a box of orange juice?   _____

㉜ What is the unit price of a box of apple juice?   _____

㉝ What is the cost per kilogram for the birthday cake?   _____

ACTIVITY

Answer the questions. Write the ratios in simplest form.

① What is the ratio of the free balloons to the paid balloons?   _____

② If Louis buys 30 balloons, how many free balloons will he get?   _____

③ There are 16 balloons in a bag. What is the ratio of paid balloons to free balloons in that bag?   _____

Buy 6 get 2 free

ISBN: 978-1-927042-15-1

WORDS TO LEARN

Pattern rule – a rule that describes a pattern

e.g.   1   3   7   15   31 . . .   The pattern rule is double the previous term and add 1.

$\times 2+1$ $\times 2+1$ $\times 2+1$ $\times 2+1$

Equation – a mathematical statement with equivalent values on either side of the equal sign

Think : 🐭 + 10 = 95

🐭 = 85

I weigh 85 g.

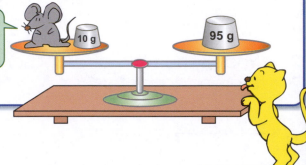

Read what the animals say.   Help them complete the number patterns.

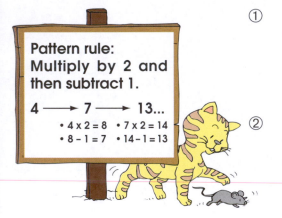

Pattern rule:
Multiply by 2 and then subtract 1.

4 ⟶ 7 ⟶ 13...
• 4 x 2 = 8   • 7 x 2 = 14
• 8 – 1 = 7   • 14 – 1 = 13

①

Multiply by 3 and then add 1.

3 ____ ____ ____ ____ ____

②

Subtract 2 and then multiply by 2.

12 ____ ____ ____ ____ ____

Look for the patterns.   Describe the rules and extend the patterns.

③   2 3 6 15 42   ⬭ ⬭ ⬭

Pattern rule: _____

④   8 17 35 71 143   ⬭ ⬭ ⬭

Pattern rule: _____

⑤   532 276 148 84 52   ⬭ ⬭ ⬭

Pattern rule: _____

The aliens have recorded their heights. Help them complete the graph to show the pattern of their heights. Then answer the questions.

⑥

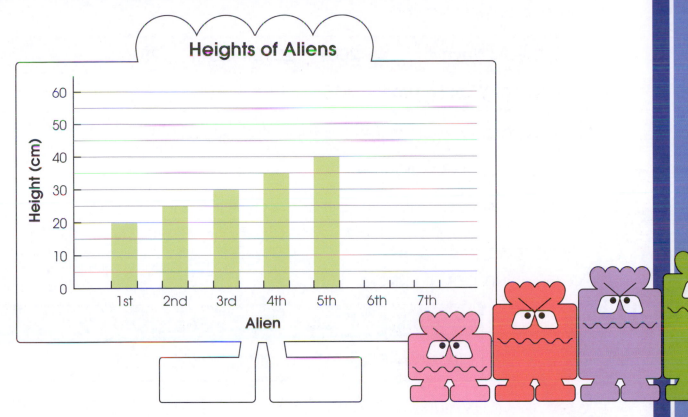

Heights of Aliens

⑦ What is the height of the 7th alien? _____

⑧ Which alien is 35 cm in height? _____

⑨ Which alien is 10 cm taller than the 3rd alien? _____

⑩ How tall is the 9th alien? _____

⑪ Describe the pattern of the heights of the aliens.

_____

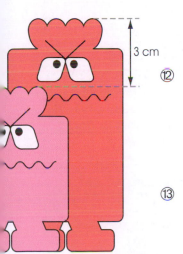

3 cm

If the aliens each have grown by 3 cm, complete the table to show their new heights. Then answer the question.

⑫ The new heights of aliens:

Alien	1st	2nd	3rd	4th	5th	6th	7th
New Height (cm)							

⑬ Do the new heights of the aliens follow a pattern? If so, what pattern do they follow?

_____

ISBN: 978-1-927042-15-1

14 The children are in a wax museum. The data in each table follows a pattern. Help them complete the tables and answer the questions.

⑭ Number of wax figures:

a.

Year	2009	2010	2011	2012		
No. of Wax Figures	145	170	195	220		

b. How many wax figures will there be by 2015?

_____ wax figures

c. In which year will there be 345 wax figures in the museum?

_____

⑮ Number of visitors:

a.

Month	Jul	Aug	Sep	Oct		
No. of Visitors	1800	2000	2300	2700		

b. How many people will visit the museum in January next year?

_____ people

c. In which month next year will 7200 people visit the museum?

_____

Find the unknown in each equation.

⑯ $\bigcirc\!\!-8=2$

$\bigcirc =$ _____

⑰ $6+\square=9$

$\square =$ _____

⑱ $6 \times \bigcirc = 30$

$\bigcirc =$ _____

⑲ $\bigcirc \div 2 = 3$

$\bigcirc =$ _____

⑳ $\bigcirc + 9 = 17$

$\bigcirc =$ _____

㉑ $\bigcirc \times 4 = 28$

$\bigcirc =$ _____

Use the "Guess-and-Test" method to find the unknown.

e.g. $6 + \bigcirc = 10$

Guess	$\bigcirc = 3$	$\bigcirc = 4$
Test	$6 + 3 = 9$ ✗	$6 + 4 = 10$ ✓

$\bigcirc = 4$

ISBN: 978-1-927042-15-1

Write an equation for each statement. Then find the unknown.

㉒ 6 more than a number y is 11.

The number is _____ .

㉓ 2 times a number c is 8.

The number is _____ .

㉔ 8 less than a number k is 20.

The number is _____ .

㉕ A number b divided by 9 is 5.

The number is _____ .

㉖ 5 plus a number m is 17.

The number is _____ .

㉗ A number g times 4 is 32.

The number is _____ .

㉘ Take away 3 from a number u is 4.

The number is _____ .

㉙ A number a multiplied by 6 is 24.

The number is _____ .

ACTIVITY

Write a mathematical expression for each statement and answer the question.

Brother Worm is y cm long.

① Sister Worm is 3 times as long as Brother Worm. _____

② Cousin Worm is 4 cm longer than Brother Worm. _____

③ Baby Worm is 2 cm shorter than Sister Worm. _____

④ Who is the longest? _____

ISBN: 978-1-927042-15-1

15 Transformations and Coordinates

Transformation – a change in a figure resulting in a different position or orientation
  Transformations include translation (slide), reflection (flip), and rotation (turn).

Coordinates – an ordered pair used to describe a location on a grid
  The order of a pair is expressed as (units across, units up).

The green triangle is the translated image of the red triangle. It is 2 units up and 3 units left from the red one.

The coordinates of the vertices of the green triangle are (3,4), (4,2), and (2,2).

Draw the images of the shapes. Then answer the questions.

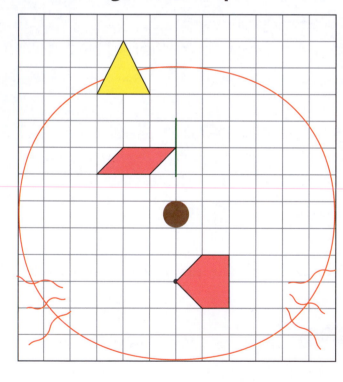

① a. Translate the triangle 1 unit down and 5 units right and colour it pink.

   b. Flip the parallelogram over the green line and colour it blue.

   c. Rotate the pentagon a half turn about • and colour it purple.

② Do the parallelograms have the same area?

_____

③ If the area of the yellow triangle is 2 square units, what is the area of the pink triangle? _____

④ If the coordinates of the turn centre are (6,3), what are the coordinates of the vertices of the purple pentagon?

_____

Read what Frankie the Farmer says. Help him plot his field on the grid and find the missing vertex. Then answer the questions.

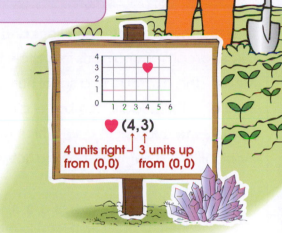

I have a field in the shape of a parallelogram. The coordinates of three vertices of my field are (1,0), (2,3), and (6,3). What are the coordinates of the 4th vertex?

⑤

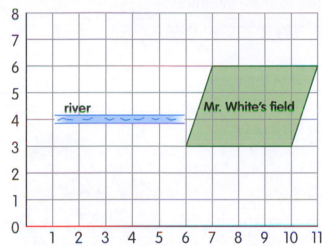

The coordinates of the 4th vertex are _____ .

⑥ The area of Frankie's field is _____ square units.

⑦ If you reflect Frankie's field over the river, you can find Mr. Beth's field. Draw the reflected image. Then write the coordinates of the vertices of Mr. Beth's field.

_____

⑧ What transformation can you do to Frankie's field so that Mr. White's field is its transformed image? Describe the transformation.

_____

A C T I V I T Y

Draw the line of reflection.

The brown figure is the reflected image of the yellow one.

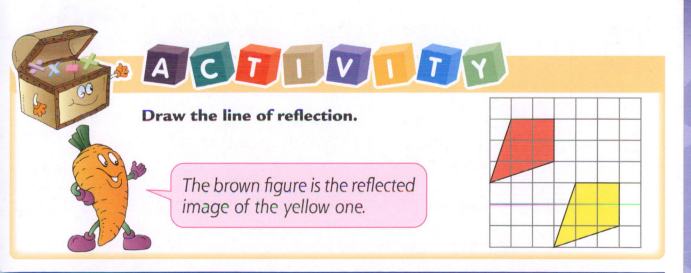

ISBN: 978-1-927042-15-1

16 Graphs and Probability

Line graph – a graph using lines and points to show information

Circle graph – using parts in a circle to show information about a whole

Mean – the average of a set of numbers

Median – the middle number of a sorted set of numbers

Mode – the number in a set which occurs most often

Probability – a number showing how likely it is that an event will happen

Numbers on the cards: 8, 6, 2, 8
Put them in order from least to greatest: 2, 6, 8, 8
Mean: $(2 + 6 + 8 + 8) \div 4 = 6$
Median: $(6 + 8) \div 2 = 7$
Mode: 8

Judy has 4 cards. She lets me pick one.

The probability of picking a 2 is $\frac{1}{4}$.

See how many blocks Joseph has. Help him complete the table. Then use a bar graph and a circle graph to show the data and answer the questions.

①

Colour	Green	Purple	Red
No. of Blocks	4		
Fraction of the Whole	$\frac{1}{4}$		

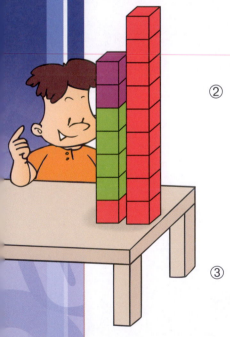

②

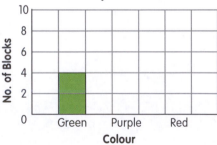

Joseph's Blocks

Joseph's Blocks

③ Joseph wants to know what fraction of the blocks are red. Which graph should he refer to?

_____

④ Joseph wants to know how many more red blocks than purple blocks he has. Which graph should he refer to?

_____

Use a line graph to show the number of sandwiches sold in the past few days. Then answer the questions.

Day	Number of Tuna Sandwiches Sold	Number of Chicken Sandwiches Sold
SUN	75	80
MON	50	10
TUE	30	25
WED	40	40
THU	50	55

⑤

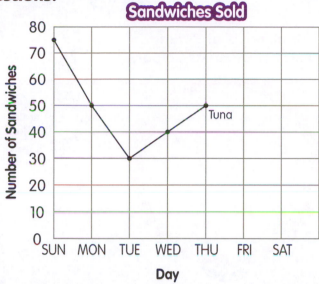

Sandwiches Sold

Tuna

⑥ The mean of tuna sandwiches sold is

_____ .

⑦ The median of chicken sandwiches sold is

_____ .

When there is more than 1 line on a graph, remember to label the lines.

⑧ The mode of tuna sandwiches sold is _____ .

⑨ Follow the trends to find how many chicken sandwiches and tuna sandwiches will be sold on Saturday.

_____ chicken sandwiches; _____ tuna sandwiches

Put each set of data in order from least to greatest. Then find its mean, median, and mode.

⑩ 64 cups   24 cups   73 cups   64 cups   24 cups
70 cups   24 cups

_____

Mean: _____
Median: _____
Mode: _____

⑪ 21 bags   15 bags   18 bags   18 bags   15 bags
15 bags

_____

Mean: _____
Median: _____
Mode: _____

ISBN: 978-1-927042-15-1

16

Johnny the Monkey is going to pick an apple. Write the probability in fractions in simplest form. Then colour the circle graph to match the probability.

⑫ The probability of picking

a. a green apple:

_____

b. a red apple:

_____

c. a golden apple:

_____

⑬ Probability of Picking Apples of Different Colours

Colour the pictures to match each situation.

⑭

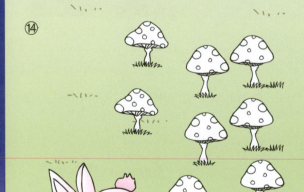

The probability of picking a yellow mushroom is $\frac{3}{8}$.

The probability of picking a red mushroom is $\frac{1}{2}$.

The probability of picking a purple mushroom is $\frac{1}{8}$.

⑮ The probability of picking a red flower is $\frac{2}{5}$.

The probability of picking a yellow flower is $\frac{1}{2}$.

The probability of picking a purple flower is $\frac{1}{10}$.

 Canadian Curriculum MathSmart (Grade 6)　ISBN: 978-1-927042-15-1

The girls want to buy some chips. Help them complete the tree diagram to show all the choices. Answer the questions.

⑯

| Brand | Packaging | Flavour |

Rays ⟨ Can ⟨ Barbecue / Ketchup / Sour Cream & Onion

Bag

⑰ How many choices are there in all? _____

⑱ How many choices are there in Ray's products? _____

⑲ How many choices are ketchup flavoured? _____

⑳ What is the probability of a customer choosing

    a. a bag of barbecue-flavoured chips? _____

    b. a can of chips? _____

ACTIVITY

Answer the questions.

① When a coin is tossed 3 times, the probability of getting 2H and 1T is _____ .

② When a coin is tossed 4 times, the probability of getting 3H and 1T is _____ .

> A coin has 2 sides: Head (H) and Tail (T)
>
> When a coin is tossed three times, there are 8 possible outcomes.

ISBN: 978-1-927042-15-1

Final Test

Rewrite as percents. (4 marks)

① $\dfrac{7}{10}$ = _____

② $9\dfrac{1}{4}$ = _____

③ 2.83 = _____

④ 0.17 = _____

Find the answers. (7 marks)

⑤
$$\begin{array}{r} 8.2\,3\,9 \\ +\ 1.6\,7\,8 \\ \hline \end{array}$$

⑥
$$\begin{array}{r} 6.0\,0\,9 \\ -\ 3.7\,7\,3 \\ \hline \end{array}$$

⑦
$$\begin{array}{r} 7.2\,8\,7 \\ \times\qquad 6 \\ \hline \end{array}$$

⑧ 6.986 ÷ 7 = _____

⑨ 3.4 x 1.9 = _____

⑩ 9.4 ÷ 0.2 = _____

⑪ 8.2 x 1.6 = _____

Solve the problems. (6 marks)

⑫ Find the volume of each solid.

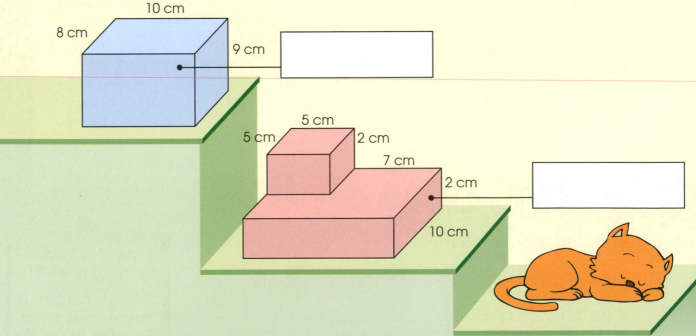

⑬ The base area of a prism is 16 m². If the
height of the prism is 8 m, what is its volume?

_____

ISBN: 978-1-927042-15-1

Look at the picture. Write each ratio in simplest form. (8 marks)

⑭ Boys to girls:

_____

⑮ Boys to all children:

_____

⑯ Girls wearing pants to girls wearing skirts:

_____

⑰ Children with blonde hair to children with dark hair:

_____

Write an equivalent ratio for each ratio. (4 marks)

⑱ 3:7 _____

⑲ 12:6 _____

⑳ 18:24 _____

㉑ 9:4 _____

Draw pictures on the spinner to match the probabilities. Then write a fraction in simplest form to complete the sentence. (4 marks)

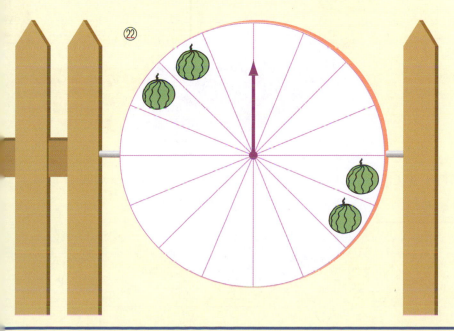

The probability of landing on

- 🍎 : $\frac{1}{4}$

- 🍊 : $\frac{3}{8}$

- 🍌 : $\frac{1}{8}$

㉓ The probability of landing on 🍉 is _____ .

Find and write the answers in simplest form. Show your work. (8 marks)

㉔ $\dfrac{5}{9} + \dfrac{1}{9} =$

㉕ $\dfrac{11}{12} - \dfrac{5}{12} =$

㉖ $\dfrac{2}{3} - \dfrac{1}{6} =$

㉗ $\dfrac{3}{10} + \dfrac{1}{2} =$

Draw the shapes on the grid. Then answer the questions. (8 marks)

㉘ The coordinates of the vertices of a quadrilateral are (1,7), (3,7), (3,5), and (1,4). Plot it on the grid and colour it yellow.

㉙ Reflect the quadrilateral over the green line and colour it blue.

㉚ Rotate the blue shape $\dfrac{1}{4}$ counterclockwise turn about (7,4) and colour it orange.

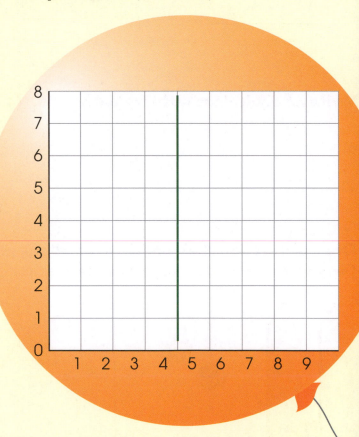

㉛ Do the shapes on the grid have the same area?

_____

Canadian Curriculum MathSmart (Grade 6)   ISBN: 978-1-927042-15-1

Look at the picture. Find the unit price of each item. (4 marks)

Unit Price

32  .... $

33  .... $

34  .... $

35  .... $

2 for $6.82   3 for $5.40
4 for $12.48   6 for $7.92

Help the children solve the problems. (10 marks)

36 Judy can run 28.98 m in 9 s. What is her speed?

_____

37 Kevin runs at a speed of 2.94 m/s for 6 s. What is the distance covered by him?

_____

38 Leo runs at a speed of 3.14 m/s for 3 s and 2.85 m/s for 8 s. What is the total distance covered by him?

_____

39 What is the area of each shape on the flag?

A :_____   B :_____

A
8 cm
10 cm
15 cm

B
11 cm
9 cm
4 cm

ISBN: 978-1-927042-15-1

Final Test

Complete the tree diagram to show all kinds of new books. Then answer the questions. (9 marks)

⑩ **Language**   **Type**   **Cover**

```
                          Hardcover
              Fiction
English                   Paperback

              Non-fiction
```

New Books

☆ **Language** ☆
English
French
Spanish

☆ **Type** ☆
Fiction
Non-fiction

☆ **Cover** ☆
Hardcover
Paperback

⑪ How many kinds of books are there? _____

⑫ How many kinds of books are in French? _____

⑬ What is the probability of a child choosing

    a. a hardcover English fiction? _____

    b. a Spanish fiction? _____

    c. a paperback? _____

Write an equation for each statement. Then find the unknown. (4 marks)

⑭ A number k divided by 5 is 7.   ⑮ The sum of a number p and 8 is 24.

The table shows the distances Alex the Alien travelled at different times from Planet A to Planet B. Follow the pattern to help Alex complete the table and answer the questions. (4 marks)

㊻ a. Distance from Planet A

Time	9:00 a.m.	9:15 a.m.	9:30 a.m.	9:45 a.m.	10:00 a.m.	10:15 a.m.
Distance (km)	8.5	16	23.5	31		

b. What time will Alex be 61 km from Planet A?

_____

c. What will be the distance between Alex and Planet A at 11:15 a.m.?

_____

Make a line graph to show how many aliens visited Planet A and Planet B in the past few days. Then answer the questions. (6 marks)

Alien Visitors

Day	Planet A	Planet B
SUN	95	15
MON	20	35
TUE	50	50
WED	60	50
THU	70	50

㊼

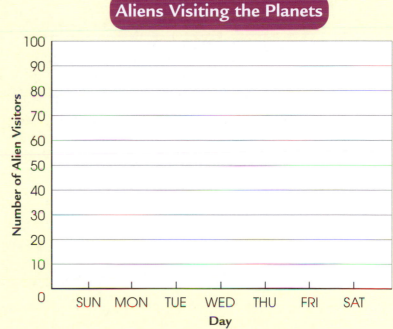

Aliens Visiting the Planets

Number of Alien Visitors

100 90 80 70 60 50 40 30 20 10 0

SUN MON TUE WED THU FRI SAT

Day

㊽ Find the mean of alien visitors to Planet A. _____

㊾ Find the median of alien visitors to Planet B. _____

㊿ Describe the number of aliens visiting Planet B in the past five days.

_____

Find the weight of each bag of candies. Then find the mean and median weight of the group. (5 marks)

51 a.

1 kg + 5 g

_____ g

b.

820 g + 4000 mg

_____ g

c.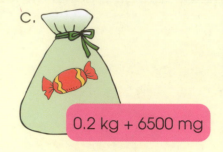

0.2 kg + 6500 mg

_____ g

52 The mean weight is _____ g.

53 The median weight is _____ g.

Help Amy solve the problems. (9 marks)

54 What is the ratio of stars to the total number of shapes?

55 Amy completed part of her journey in $\frac{4}{5}$ h and the remainder in $\frac{1}{2}$ h. How long did it take her to complete the whole journey?

56 Amy wants to buy her dog a sausage. If 12 sausages cost $4.08, how much does Amy need to pay for the sausage?

Score

100

1 Operations with Whole Numbers

1. ten thousands ; 30 000 ; 100 000 + 30 000 + 200 + 1
2. hundred thousands ; 600 000 ; 600 000 + 100 + 10 + 3
3. thousands ; 2000 ; 700 000 + 80 000 + 2000 + 3

4. < 5. < 6. <
7. > 8. > 9. <

10. 966 430 11. 554 739 12. 604 762
13. 780 653 14. 849 15. 1249
16. 3763 17. 34 109 18. 39 062
19. 36 233 20. 4884 21. 14 811
22. 5099

23. 4005 ; 1000 + 1000 + 1000 + 1000 = 4000
24. 7640 ; 3000 + 1000 + 1000 + 3000 = 8000
25. 29 260 ; 38 000 − 8000 = 30 000

26.
```
    1 3 3    ; 1596
  x    1 2
    2 6 6
  1 3 3 0
  1 5 9 6
```

27.
```
    1 2 4
  x    3 9
  1 1 1 6
  3 7 2 0
  4 8 3 6
```
28.
```
    7 6 8
  x    2 5
  3 8 4 0
1 5 3 6 0
1 9 2 0 0
```
29.
```
    9 8 1
  x    4 7
  6 8 6 7
3 9 2 4 0
4 6 1 0 7
```

30. 20 570 31. 45 408
32. 19 293 33. 6552
34. 11 853 ; 440 x 30 = 13 200
35. 40 092 ; 770 x 50 = 38 500
36. 27 765 ; 620 x 50 = 31 000

37. 134 ; 134 ;
```
        1 3 4
  1 2 ) 1 6 0 8
        1 2
          4 0
          3 6
            4 8
            4 8
```

38.
```
        1 0 2
  4 6 ) 4 6 9 2
        4 6
          9 2
          9 2
```
39.
```
        4 1
  3 9 ) 1 5 9 9
        1 5 6
            3 9
            3 9
```

40.
```
        3 3 8 R17
  2 5 ) 8 4 6 7
        7 5
          9 6
          7 5
          2 1 7
          2 0 0
            1 7
```
41.
```
        1 6 4 R1
  1 8 ) 2 9 5 3
        1 8
        1 1 5
        1 0 8
            7 3
            7 2
              1
```

42.
```
        2 9 1 R7
  2 3 ) 6 7 0 0
        4 6
        2 1 0
        2 0 7
            3 0
            2 3
              7
```

43. 189 44. 236R14
45. 137R20 46. 96
47. 122R8 ; 36 x 125 = 4500
48. ✔ ; 24 x 216 = 5184
49. 1080 ÷ 60 = 18 ; 18
50. 452 + 386 + 415 + 339 = 1592 ; 1592
51. 678 x 11 = 7458 ; 7458
52. 1592 − 678 = 914 ; 914
53. 914 x 25 = 22 850 ; 22 850
54. 22 850 − 7458 = 15 392 ; 15 392
55. 14 ; 42 ; 56 56. 12 ; 11 ; 1
57. 83 ; 8 ; 75 58. 69 + 10 ; 79
59. 91 − 68 ; 23 60. 90 − 3 x 28 = 6 ; 6
61. 4 x 3 + 19 = 31 ; 31

Activity
9

2 Brackets

1. 4 ; 7 ; 18 ; 18 2. 20 ; 35 ; 175 ; 175
3. 17 − 4 ; 13 4. 4 x 7 ; 28
5. 48 ÷ 3 ; 16 6. 14 + 14 ; 28
7. 76 ÷ 2 ; 38 8. 20 x 8 ; 160
9. 99 + (33 ÷ 11) = 102 10. (108 − 3) x 9 = 945
11. 14 x (7 + 6) = 182 12. 256 ÷ (16 − 8) = 32
13. 100 − (36 ÷ 4) = 91 14. 39 + (2 x 17) = 73
15. 3 ; 5 ; 21 ; 35 ; 56
16. 18 ; 7 ; 72 ; 28 ; 44
17. 31 ; 15 ; 279 ; 135 ; 144
18. 50 ; 2 ; 250 ; 10 ; 260

Activity
1. 546 2. 531 ; 59 = 60 − 1
3. 544 ; 68 = 70 − 2 4. 294 ; 42 = 40 + 2
5. 415 ; 83 = 80 + 3

3 Integers

1. 12 ; -3 ; 0 ; 8 ; 156 ; -8 ; 20
2. -6 3. +15 4. +36
5. -14 6. +9 7. -87
8. > 9. < 10. <
11. > 12. > 13. <
14. -6, -3, 0, 2, 5
15. -4, 1, 3, 5, 7
16. -5, -3, 0, 1, 6
17. A : -2°C B : 3°C C : 9°C
    D : 1°C E : -3°C F : 4°C
18. C 19. 2
20. 4 21. C
22. E, A, D, B, F, C

Activity
1. -1 ; 5 2. 0 ; -4
3. -6 ; -9

4 Multiples and Factors

1. 6 ; 8 ; 10 ; 12 ; 14 ; 16
2. 9 ; 12 ; 15
3. 5, 10, 15, 20, 25, 30
4. 7, 14, 21, 28, 35, 42
5. 9, 18, 27, 36, 45, 54
6a. 4 : 4, 8, 12, 16, 20, 24, 28, 32
    6 : 6, 12, 18, 24, 30, 36, 42, 48
b. 12, 24 c. 12

7a. 8 : 8, 16, 24, 32, 40, 48, 56, 64

    10 : 10, 20, 30, 40, 50, 60, 70, 80

  b. 40   c. 40

8. 20, 40, 60, 80 ; 20

9. 9, 18, 27, 36 ; 9

10. 6, 12, 18, 24 ; 6

11. 14   12. 7

13. 2   14. 1

15. 1, 2, 7, 14

16. 12 ; 6 ; 4 ; 1, 2, 3, 4, 6, 12

17. 20 ; 10 ; 5 ; 1, 2, 4, 5, 10, 20

18. 1, 2, 3, 4, 6, 8, 12, 24

19. 1, 2, 3, 5, 6, 10, 15, 30

20. 1, 2, 4, 8, 16, 32

21. 1, 2, 3, 4, 6, 9, 12, 18, 36

22. 1, 2, 4, 5, 8, 10, 20, 40

23a. 20 : 1, 2, 4, 5, 10, 20

     28 : 1, 2, 4, 7, 14, 28

  b. 1, 2, 4   c. 4

24a. 25 : 1, 5, 25

     45 : 1, 3, 5, 9, 15, 45

  b. 1, 5   c. 5

25. 1, 5 ; 5   26. 1, 2, 4, 8 ; 8

Activity

    6 ; 4 ; 5

5   Composite and Prime Numbers

1. 7 ; prime   2. 5 ; prime

3. 4 ; composite   4. composite

5. prime   6. composite

7. prime   8. composite

9. composite

10.   11.

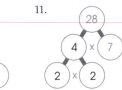

    2 x 3 x 7   2 x 2 x 7

12.   13.

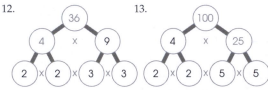

   2 x 2 x 3 x 3   2 x 2 x 5 x 5

14. 2 x 3 x 11   15. 2 x 2 x 13

16. 2 x 37   17. 2 x 2 x 2 x 2 x 2 x 3

18. 3 x 3 x 3 x 3   19. 2 x 2 x 2 x 11

20. 2 x 2 x 2 x 2 x 2 21. 2 x 2 x 2 x 5

22. 2 x 2 x 2 x 3   23. 2 x 29

24. 2, 3, 5 ;   25. 2, 2, 2, 2, 3 ;

    3, 3, 5 ;   2, 2, 2, 3, 3 ;

    3, 5 ;   2, 2, 2, 3 ;

    3, 5 ; 15   2, 2, 2, 3 ; 24

26. 2 x 2 x 3 ; 2 x 2 x 5 ; 4

27. 3 x 5 ; 2 x 2 x 3 x 5 ; 15

28. 2 x 2 x 2 ; 2 x 2 x 2 x 5 ; 8

29. 2 x 2 x 2 x 7 ; 2 x 2 x 2 x 2 x 2 x 2 ; 8

30. 2, 5 ;   31. 5 ;

    2, 3, 11 ;   2, 5, 5 ;

    2, 3, 5, 11 ;   2, 5, 5, 7 ;

    330   350

32. 3, 5 ;

    3, 7 ;

    3, 5, 7 ;

    105

33. 30   34. 40

35. 72   36. 54

37. 66   38. 216

Activity

1-3. (Suggested answers)

  1. 5, 19   2. 29, 47

  3. 31, 59

6   Time, Speed, and Distance

1. A : 13:30   B : 12:15

   C : 16:45   D : 03:18

   E : 19:53   F : 21:27

2.   3.

  2:20:10 p.m.   12:47:13 a.m.

4. No   5. 40 min

6. 12:15   7. 16:39

8. 68 min or 1 h 8 min

9. CP826   10. 38 min

11. (Suggested answers)

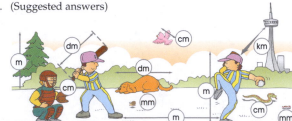

12. 630   13. 4000

14. 92   15. 57

16. 9.7   17. 2.3

18. 5.5   19. 3.71

20. 0.105   21. 80

22. 1270   23. 635

24. 1905

ISBN: 978-1-927042-15-1

25.

Race	Distance	Time	Speed
1	700 km	2 h	$\frac{700}{2}$ = 350 (km/h)
2	347 000 m	1 h	$\frac{347}{1}$ = 347 (km/h)
3	414 km	1.2 h	345 km/h
4	531 km	1.5 h	354 km/h

26. Race 4

27. 5 more km   **28.** 414 km/h

29. 540 s   **30.** 12:07 p.m.

Activity

   80.8 m

7 Perimeter and Area

1. A : 5 cm ; 3 cm ; 15 cm²
   B : 2 cm ; 2 cm ; 4 cm²
   C : 3 cm ; 4 cm ; 12 cm²
   D : 6 cm ; 3 cm ; 9 cm²
   E : 5 cm ; 4 cm ; 10 cm²
   F : 4 cm ; 2 cm ; 4 cm²

2. Yes   3. Yes

4. A : 5 cm ; 6 cm ; 30 cm² ; 24 cm
   B : 7 cm ; 12 cm ; 84 cm² ; 40 cm
   C : 28 cm ; 38 cm ; 1064 cm² ; 142 cm
   D : 12 m ; 9 m ; 108 m² ; 44 m
   E : 18 km ; 3 km ; 54 km² ; 43 km

5. (Suggested answer)

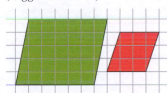

6. A : 4.6 cm ; 7.5 cm ; 17.25 cm² ; 20.9 cm
   B : 12 cm ; 7 cm ; 42 cm² ; 31 cm
   C : 5 cm ; 5 cm ; 12.5 cm² ; 20.7 cm
   D : 3 m ; 4 m ; 6 m² ; 13.9 m

7. D, B, A, C

8. B, C, A, D

9. (Suggested answer)

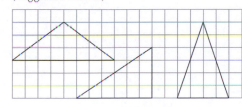

10. 13   11. 64

12. 500

Activity

   32

8 2-D Shapes and 3-D Figures

1.    2.

3. (Suggested answers)

a.   b.

c.

4. 2 ; 5 ; 2
   3 ; 4 ; 4

5. (Suggested answers)

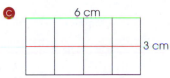

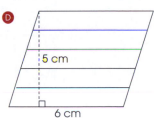

6-7. (Draw shapes with the same sizes and shapes as the given ones.)

8. 1 ; 4 ; 2 ; 6

9. (Suggested answers)

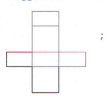   ;   ;

10. A ; C   11. C

12. A ; C

13.

Activity

Yes, since they are different sizes but the corresponding angles are the same.

Midway Test

1. 8 ; 7 ; 72 ; 63 ; 135
2. 3 ; 3 ; 348 ; 87 ; 261
3. 34 ÷ 17 ;
   2
4. 18 + 80 ;
   98
5. 110 – 60 ;
   50
6. 50 ÷ 2 ;
   25
7. 7 : 7, 14, 21, 28, 35, 42, 49, 56
   8 : 8, 16, 24, 32, 40, 48, 56, 64
   56 ; 56
8. 6 : 6, 12, 18, 24, 30, 36, 42, 48
   9 : 9, 18, 27, 36, 45, 54, 63, 72
   18, 36 ; 18
9.
```
        366
   25)9150
        75
        165
        150
         150
         150
```
10.
```
        76R21
   37)2833
        259
        243
        222
         21
```
11.
```
      782
   x   32
     1564
    23460
    25024
```
12. 32 665
13. 421R2
14. 4727
15. 222R1
16. 90 km/h
17. 225 km
18. 18:05
19. 20 : 1, 2, 4, 5, 10, 20
    32 : 1, 2, 4, 8, 16, 32
    1, 2, 4 ;
    4
20. 18 : 1, 2, 3, 6, 9, 18
    24 : 1, 2, 3, 4, 6, 8, 12, 24
    1, 2, 3, 6 ;
    6
21. -3°C
22. No
23. Tomorrow
24-25. (Suggested answers)

24.

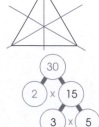

25.

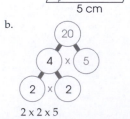

26a.

```
        30
    2  x  15
        3  x  5
```
2 x 3 x 5

b.

```
        20
    4  x  5
    2  x  2
```
2 x 2 x 5

c.

```
    25
  5  x  5
```
5 x 5

27. 10
28. 5
29. 60
30. 100
31. 6
32. 3
33. 35 069
34. 900
35. 87 848
36. 2465
37. 80 cm² ; 44 cm
38. 48 m² ; 32 m
39. (Suggested answer)

| Parallelogram | Triangle |

40.
41.
42.
43.

44. 13 x 927 = 12 051 ; He will earn $12 051.
45. 13 000 – 4662 = 8338 ; He will earn $8338.
46. 3348 ÷ 31 = 108 ; 108 pizzas are sold in a day.

9 Volume and Mass

1. A : 36 m³
   B : 768 cm³
   C : 255 cm³
   D : 420 cm³
   E : 297 cm³
2. 324
3. 1750 ; 440
4. 9008
5. 4.39
6. 6145
7. 0.978
8. 17 240
9. 0.9
10. 1260
11. 2
12. George: 7500 g
    Louis: 8000 g
    Wayne: 0.995 g
    Richard: 5100 g
    Bob: 5.2 g
    Ted: 4.975 g
13. Louis
14. Wayne

Activity

162

ISBN: 978-1-927042-15-1

10 Operations with Decimals

1. 40 + 5 + 0.6 + 0.01 + 0.009 ; 45 and 619 thousandths
2. 60 + 0.2 + 0.002 ; 60 and 202 thousandths
3. 4.251
4. 4.031
5. 0.167
6. 12.029
7. 2.585
8. 0.609
9. 8.934
10. 4.247
11. 4.771
12. 262.3
13. 0.388
14. 0.894
15. 76.7
16. 50.51
17. 3.054
18. 0.0625
19. 0.001
20. 2 ; 4 ; 7 ; 0 ; 2.47
21. 2.52
22. 2.600
23. 14.004
24. 11.286
25. 9.31
26. 26.145
27. 32.334
28. 11.284
29. 18.615
30. 3.6
31. 6.02
32. 1.92

33. 75 ; 5 ; 5

$$15\overline{)75}$$
$$\underline{75}$$
result: 5

34. $= \dfrac{32.4 \times 10}{0.4 \times 10}$

$$4\overline{)324}$$
$$\underline{32}$$
$$4$$
$$\underline{4}$$
result: 81

$= \dfrac{324}{4}$

$= 81$

35. $= \dfrac{1.6 \times 100}{0.08 \times 100}$

$$8\overline{)160}$$
$$\underline{160}$$
result: 20

$= \dfrac{160}{8}$

$= 20$

36. 177
37. 15
38. 0.17
39. 15.5
40. 6.2
41. 14
42. 18
43. 9
44. 4.02
45. 20.8
46. 4.414
47. 5.224
48. 13.3
49. 4.752
50. 26.7
51. 78.72
52. 7.423
53. 75.099
54. 64.4
55. 1.044

Activity

1. 2
2. 12.14
3. 5.3
4. 8.86
5. 3.4
6. 0

11 Operations with Fractions

1. $3\frac{2}{3}$
2. $\frac{31}{7}$
3. $\frac{9}{5}$
4. $\frac{13}{5}$
5. $1\frac{4}{9}$
6. $3\frac{1}{6}$
7. $\frac{7}{4}$
8. $2\frac{4}{7}$
9. $\frac{25}{8}$
10. $\frac{13}{2}$
11. $\frac{5}{2}$
12. $2\frac{7}{9}$
13. >
14. <
15. <
16. >
17. <
18. <
19. >
20. >
21. 3 ; 1
22. 4 ; 2
23. $\frac{6}{12}$; $\frac{1}{2}$
24. $\frac{7}{7}$; 1
25. $\frac{10}{15}$; $\frac{2}{3}$
26. $\frac{8}{20}$; $\frac{2}{5}$

27. $\frac{12}{10}$; $1\frac{1}{5}$
28. $\frac{16}{18}$; $\frac{8}{9}$
29. $1\frac{1}{3}$
30. $\frac{1}{4}$
31. $\frac{3}{5}$
32. $\frac{3}{8}$; $\frac{1}{4}$; $\frac{5}{8}$
33. $\frac{5}{6}$; $\frac{2}{3}$; $\frac{1}{6}$
34. $\frac{1}{2}$; $\frac{1}{3}$; $\frac{5}{6}$
35. $\frac{5}{6}$; $\frac{1}{3}$; $\frac{1}{2}$
36. 4 ; 5 ; $\frac{1}{2}$
37. 8 ; 5
38. $\frac{5}{8}$
39. $\frac{13}{20}$
40. $\frac{5}{6}$
41. $\frac{4}{15}$
42. $\frac{2}{5}$
43. $\frac{13}{15}$
44. $\frac{3}{16}$
45. $\frac{4}{5}$
46. $\frac{9}{16}$
47. $\frac{1}{8}$
48. $\frac{5}{6} + \frac{1}{3} = 1\frac{1}{6}$; $1\frac{1}{6}$
49. $\frac{17}{20} - \frac{3}{4} = \frac{1}{10}$; $\frac{1}{10}$
50. $\frac{9}{10} + \frac{1}{5} = 1\frac{1}{10}$; $1\frac{1}{10}$

Activity

No. of Days	1	2	3	4	5	6	7
Amount of Juice Consumed (L)	$\frac{2}{5}$	$\frac{4}{5}$	$\frac{6}{5}$	$\frac{8}{5}$	$\frac{10}{5}$	$\frac{12}{5}$	$\frac{14}{5}$

7

12 Fractions, Decimals, and Percents

1. 25%
2. 50%
3. 41%
4. 7%
5. 80%
6. 2%
7. 30%
8. 92%
9.
10.
11.
12. $\frac{71}{100}$; 0.71 ; 71%
13. $\frac{26}{100}$; 0.26 ; 26%
14. 13%
15. 57%
16. 8%
17. 35 ; 35%
18. 75 ; 75%
19. 32 ; 332%
20. 50 ; 450%
21. $1\frac{90}{100}$; 190%
22. $\frac{22}{100}$; 22%
23. $2\frac{25}{100}$; 225%
24. $1\frac{85}{100}$; 185%
25. $\frac{19}{50}$
26. $\frac{3}{5}$
27. $\frac{2}{25}$
28. $\frac{2}{5}$
29. $1\frac{9}{10}$
30. $2\frac{1}{2}$
31. 55 ; $\frac{11}{20}$
32. 25 ; $\frac{1}{4}$
33. 20 ; $\frac{1}{5}$
34a. 25
b. 20
c. 55
35. 20 ; 0.2
36. 5 ; 0.05
37. $\frac{77}{100}$; 0.77
38. $\frac{60}{100}$; 0.6
39. $\frac{125}{100}$; 1.25
40. $\frac{190}{100}$; 1.9
41. $\frac{142}{100}$; 1.42
42. $\frac{106}{100}$; 1.06
43. 34
44. 6
45. 80
46. 143
47. 120
48. 27
49. 604
50. 92
51. <
52. >
53. >
54. <
55. >
56. >
57. 40%, 0.55, $\frac{3}{5}$
58. 115%, 1.29, $1\frac{7}{20}$
59. 1.8%, $\frac{4}{25}$, 0.18
60. $\frac{2}{5}$; 40%

61. 50% ; 0.5 62. $\frac{1}{10}$; 0.1

63. 4% 64. 90%

Activity

1. Christmas

2a. 30% b. 50% c. 20%

13 Rate and Ratio

1. Pears: $1.96/kg Grapes: $3.28/kg
   Watermelons: $0.87/kg Apples: $1.74/kg
   Bananas: $1.07/kg Oranges: $2.62/kg

2. 4 for $1.12 3. 3 for $1.56

4. 5 for $4.40

5. 3 ; 7 6. 2:7 7. 2:3

8. 3:12 9. 2:12 10. 7:12

11-16. (Suggested answers)

11. 4:6, 6:9 12. 10:8, 15:12

13. 1:3, 3:9 14. 4:3, 16:12

15. 4:3, 56:42 16. 2:5, 8:20

17. 1:2 18. 3:8

19. 4:7 20. 3:2

21. 3:5 22. 3:4

23. 8:1 24. 9:4

25a. 5:6 b. 2:3

c. 2:5 d. 4:15

e. 1:3

26a. 4:5 b. 10:9

c. 8:9 d. 3:1

e. 1:2 f. 2:3

g. 1:3 h. 1:3

i. 10:27

27. 1:1 28. 1:2

29. 1:1 30. 1:4

31. $0.56 32. $0.49

33. $6.45/kg

Activity

1. 1:3 2. 10

3. 3:1

14 Patterns and Simple Equations

1. 10 ; 31 ; 94 ; 283 ; 850

2. 20 ; 36 ; 68 ; 132 ; 260

3. 123 ; 366 ; 1095 ;
   Subtract 1 and then multiply by 3.

4. 287 ; 575 ; 1151 ;
   Multiply by 2 and then add 1.

5. 36 ; 28 ; 24 ;
   Divide by 2 and then add 10.

6.

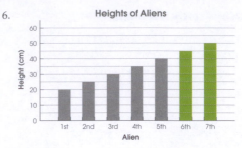

7. 50 cm 8. The 4th

9. The 5th 10. 60 cm

11. Each alien is 5 cm taller than the previous one.

12. 23 ; 28 ; 33 ; 38 ; 43 ; 48 ; 53

13. Yes, each alien is 5 cm taller than the previous one.

14a.

Year	2009	2010	2011	2012	2013	2014
No. of Wax Figures	145	170	195	220	245	270

b. 295 c. 2007

15a.

Month	Jul	Aug	Sep	Oct	Nov	Dec
No. of Visitors	1800	2000	2300	2700	3200	3800

b. 4500 c. April

16. 10 17. 3

18. 5 19. 6

20. 8 21. 7

22. 6 + y = 11 ; 5 23. 2 x c = 8 ; 4

24. k − 8 = 20 ; 28 25. b ÷ 9 = 5 ; 45

26. 5 + m = 17 ; 12 27. g x 4 = 32 ; 8

28. u − 3 = 4 ; 7 29. a x 6 = 24 ; 4

Activity

1. (3 x y) cm 2. (y + 4) cm

3. (3 x y − 2) cm 4. Sister Worm

15 Transformations and Coordinates

1.

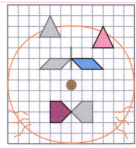

2. Yes 3. 2 square units

4. The coordinates are (4,4), (5,4), (6,3), (5,2), and (4,2).

5.

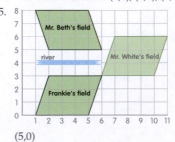

(5,0)

6. 12

7. The coordinates are (1,8), (5,8), (6,5), and (2,5).

ISBN: 978-1-927042-15-1

8. Rotation. Rotate Frankie's field $\frac{1}{2}$ turn about (6,3)./
    Translation. Translate Frankie's field 3 units up and 5 units
    right.

Activity

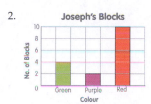

16 Graphs and Probability

1.

Colour	Green	Purple	Red
No. of Blocks	4	2	10
Fraction of the Whole	$\frac{1}{4}$	$\frac{1}{8}$	$\frac{5}{8}$

2.

3. The circle graph
4. The bar graph
5.

6. 49   7. 40
8. 50   9. 85 ; 70
10. 24 cups, 24 cups, 24 cups, 64 cups, 64 cups, 70 cups, 73 cups ;
    49 cups ; 64 cups ; 24 cups
11. 15 bags, 15 bags, 15 bags, 18 bags, 18 bags, 21 bags ;
    17 bags ; 16.5 bags ; 15 bags

12a. $\frac{1}{6}$ b. $\frac{1}{2}$ c. $\frac{1}{3}$

13.

14.

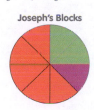

15.

16.

Brand	Packaging	Flavour
Rays	Can	Barbecue / Ketchup / Sour Cream & Onion
	Bag	Barbecue / Ketchup / Sour Cream & Onion
Twinkle	Can	Barbecue / Ketchup / Sour Cream & Onion
	Bag	Barbecue / Ketchup / Sour Cream & Onion

17. 12   18. 6

19. 4

20a. $\frac{4}{12}$ or $\frac{1}{3}$ b. $\frac{6}{12}$ or $\frac{1}{2}$

Activity

1. $\frac{3}{8}$ 2. $\frac{4}{16}$ or $\frac{1}{4}$

Final Test

1. 70%   2. 925%
3. 283%   4. 17%
5. 9.917   6. 2.236
7. 43.722   8. 0.998
9. 6.46   10. 47
11. 13.12
12. 720 cm³ ; 290 cm³   13. 128 m³
14. 1:1   15. 1:2
16. 2:3   17. 2:1
18-21. (Suggested answers)
18. 6:14   19. 2:1
20. 9:12   21. 18:8
22.

23. $\frac{1}{4}$
24. $\frac{6}{9} = \frac{2}{3}$ 25. $\frac{6}{12} = \frac{1}{2}$
26. $\frac{4}{6} - \frac{1}{6} = \frac{3}{6}$ 27. $\frac{3}{10} + \frac{5}{10} = \frac{8}{10}$
    $\quad\quad\quad = \frac{1}{2}$ $\quad\quad\quad\quad = \frac{4}{5}$

28-30.

31. Yes
32. 3.41   33. 1.80
34. 3.12   35. 1.32
36. 3.22 m/s   37. 17.64 m
38. 32.22 m
39. A : 120 cm²   B : 18 cm²

40.

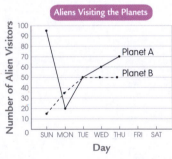

Language	Type	Cover

English
- Fiction
  - Hardcover
  - Paperback
- Non-Fiction
  - Hardcover
  - Paperback

French
- Fiction
  - Hardcover
  - Paperback
- Non-Fiction
  - Hardcover
  - Paperback

Spanish
- Fiction
  - Hardcover
  - Paperback
- Non-Fiction
  - Hardcover
  - Paperback

41. 12   42. 4

43a. $\frac{1}{12}$ b. $\frac{2}{12}$ or $\frac{1}{6}$ c. $\frac{6}{12}$ or $\frac{1}{2}$

44. $k \div 5 = 7$; The number is 35.

45. $p + 8 = 24$; The number is 16.

46a. 38.5 ; 46

b. 10:45 a.m.

c. 76 km

47.

Aliens Visiting the Planets

Planet A
Planet B

Number of Alien Visitors (0, 10, 20, 30, 40, 50, 60, 70, 80, 90, 100)

Day (SUN MON TUE WED THU FRI SAT)

48. 59 aliens   49. 50 aliens

50. The number of aliens visiting Planet B increased gradually. Starting from Tuesday, the number of visitors was the same each day.

51a. 1005   b. 824

c. 206.5

52. 678.5   53. 824

54. Number of stars:Total number of shapes = 10:25 = 2:5
The ratio is 2:5.

55. $\frac{4}{5} + \frac{1}{2} = 1\frac{3}{10}$
It took her $1\frac{3}{10}$ h to cover the whole journey.

56. $4.08 \div 12 = 0.34$
Amy needs to pay $0.34.

ISBN: 978-1-927042-15-1